This edition produced in 1994 for
Shooting Star Press Inc
230 Fifth Avenue
Suite 1212
New York, NY 10001

© Aladdin Books Ltd 1994

Designed and produced by
Aladdin Books Ltd
28 Percy Street
London W1P 9FF

Printed in the Czech Republic

ISBN 1-56924-070-1

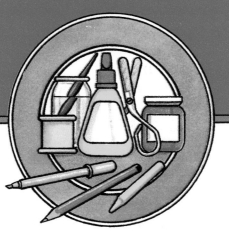

Make
it
yourself

SHOOTING STAR PRESS

About this book

The projects in this book are designed for children to make by themselves or with a group of friends. Children can follow the sequence of instructions through pictures, whether or not they can read. The text is included for the parent/teacher to give additional hints and tips.

The "What you need" panel shows clearly what is required for each project. No supervision is required – except where this symbol appears ⚠.

The materials needed for the projects are usually available in most homes or classrooms. Where certain materials may not be available, alternatives are given. It is a good idea to collect all sorts of household bits and pieces.

The level of difficulty of the projects varies slightly to cater to children of differing abilities.

 Where this symbol appears, adult help is required. Look for it.

Cutting

Children should never be given sharp knives or scissors, and for most projects in this book they are unnecessary. There are many types of children's scissors available with rounded ends. Where objects are difficult to cut – for example, potatoes or plastic dish-washing liquid bottles – an adult should supervise. These instances are marked with the danger symbol. Where a plastic bottle is specified, be sure that it does not contain any dangerous liquids such as bleach or disinfectant. Always rinse out bottles, whatever they have contained.

Gluing

Any sort of paste or glue is suitable for making most of the projects, but in certain cases a strong glue is required and this is illustrated with a red asterisk on the glue pot. An adult should supervise when strong glue is being used.

Coloring

Most projects can be successfully colored with powder paint or ordinary watercolor. For shiny or plastic surfaces use poster paint, powder paint, or tempura paint mixed with a PVA medium. Look for the AP or CP seal of approval. Where projects are to be used in water, use wax crayons to color them.

Powder paint, poster paint, and wax crayons are all nontoxic and lead-free. Alternative coloring methods are colored pencils (crayons), or felt-tip pens and pastels. Ensure that the felt-tips you use are nontoxic.

One of the simplest ways of applying color is to cut out the required shape from colored paper and glue it onto the project.

Tracing

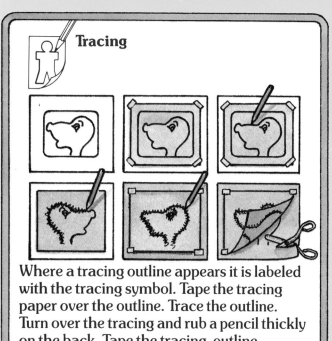

Where a tracing outline appears it is labeled with the tracing symbol. Tape the tracing paper over the outline. Trace the outline. Turn over the tracing and rub a pencil thickly on the back. Tape the tracing, outline upward, on paper or cardboard, and retrace the outline.

What you need:

What the symbols mean

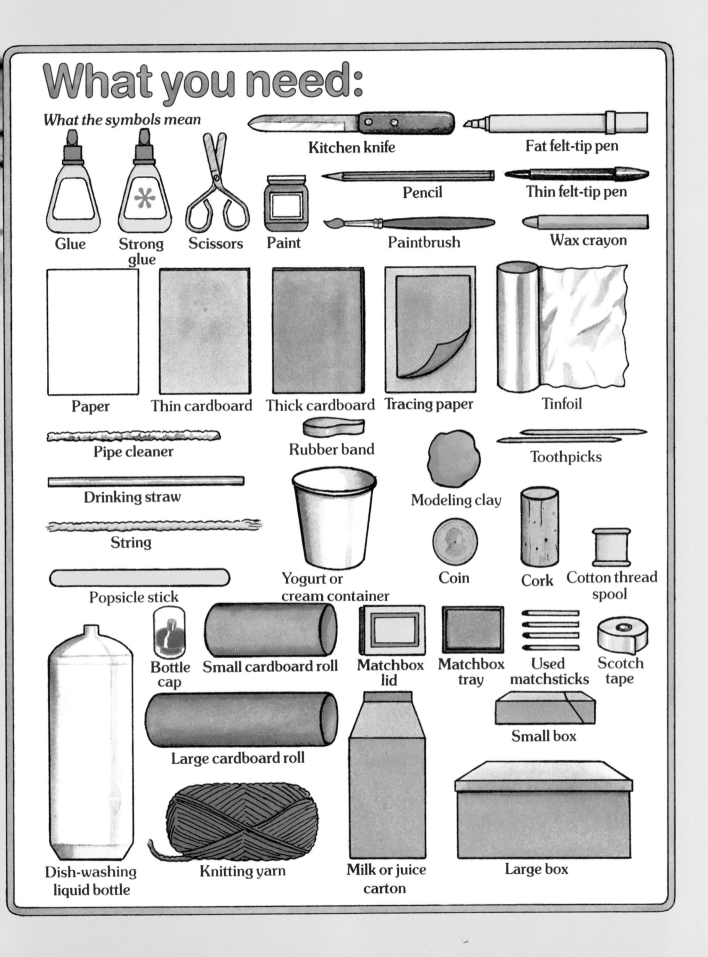

Glue

Strong glue

Scissors

Paint

Kitchen knife

Pencil

Paintbrush

Fat felt-tip pen

Thin felt-tip pen

Wax crayon

Paper

Thin cardboard

Thick cardboard

Tracing paper

Tinfoil

Pipe cleaner

Rubber band

Toothpicks

Drinking straw

Modeling clay

String

Yogurt or cream container

Coin

Cork

Cotton thread spool

Popsicle stick

Bottle cap

Small cardboard roll

Matchbox lid

Matchbox tray

Used matchsticks

Scotch tape

Large cardboard roll

Small box

Dish-washing liquid bottle

Knitting yarn

Milk or juice carton

Large box

CONTENTS

Potato Cow

- For each cow try to find a large potato for the body and a small one for the head. Or you could cut a large potato into a smaller shape for the head, if you need to.

- Use cocktail sticks, toothpicks or matchsticks for the legs and neck.

- Gently push one end of the string tail into the potato as shown and fray the other end to make it look more realistic.

- If you cannot get pipe cleaners for the horns, use pieces of matchstick instead.

What you need:

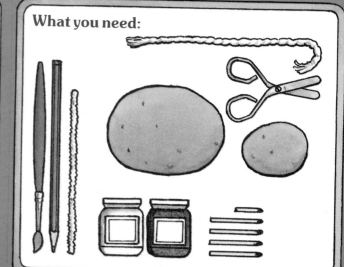

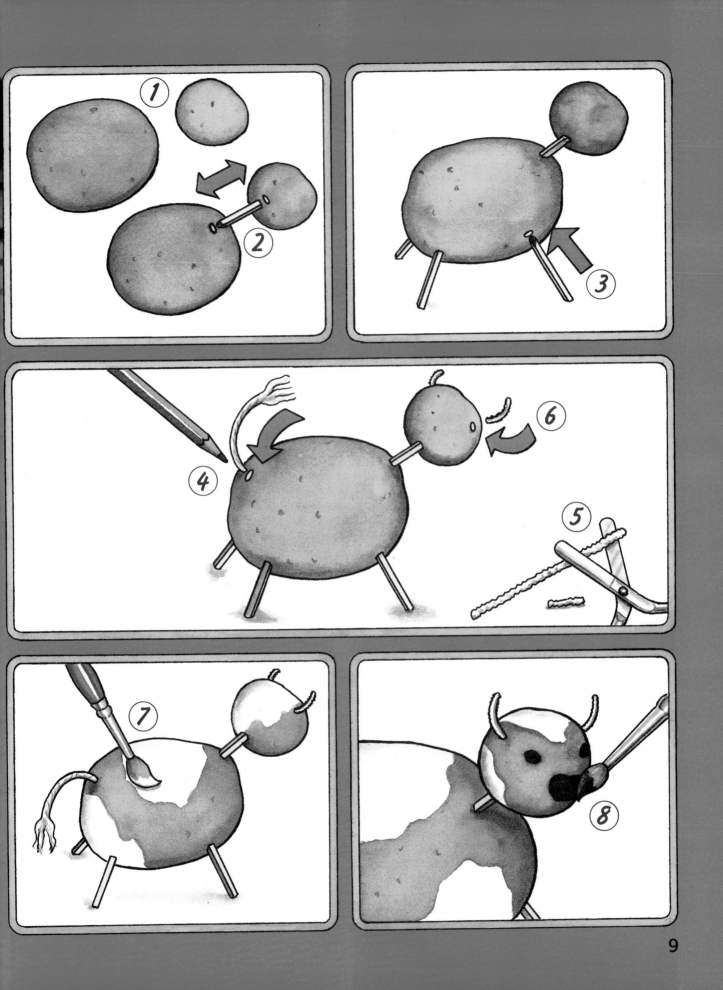

9

Spinning Snake

What you need:

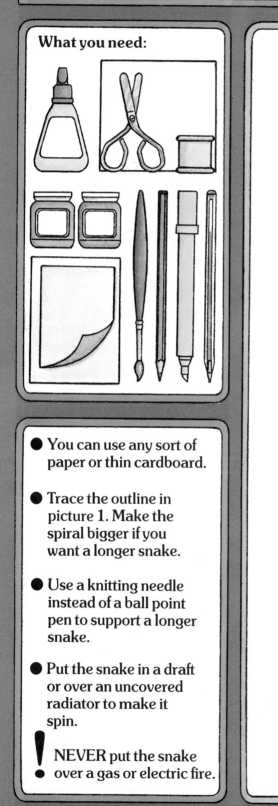

- You can use any sort of paper or thin cardboard.

- Trace the outline in picture 1. Make the spiral bigger if you want a longer snake.

- Use a knitting needle instead of a ball point pen to support a longer snake.

- Put the snake in a draft or over an uncovered radiator to make it spin.

! NEVER put the snake over a gas or electric fire.

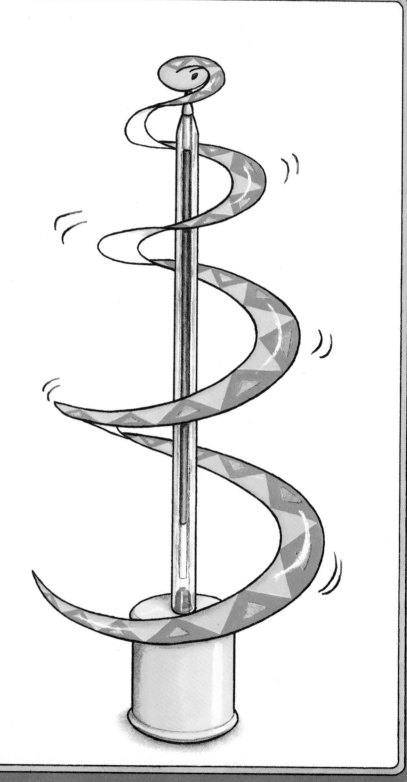

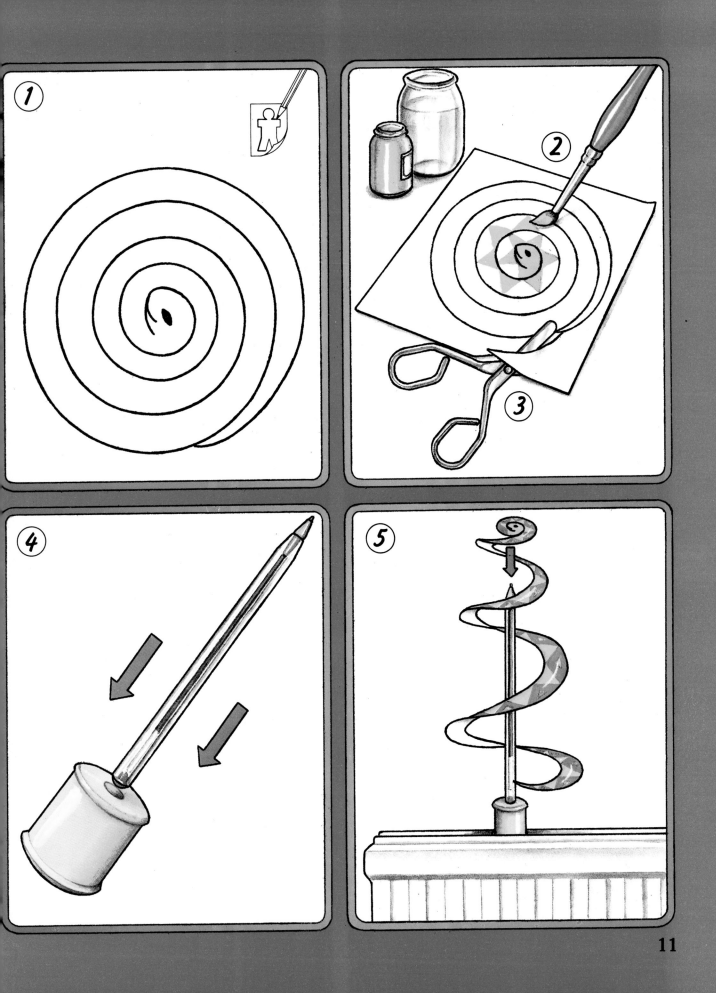

Egg Carton Bee

What you need:

- The egg carton you use for this project can be cardboard or Styrofoam.

- Trace the outline in picture 4 twice onto a paper or cardboard to make the wings.

- Half an egg carton will make two bees.

- Put cotton thread or thin string through the middle section of the bee, securing it with a knot on the inside, and hang it as a mobile.

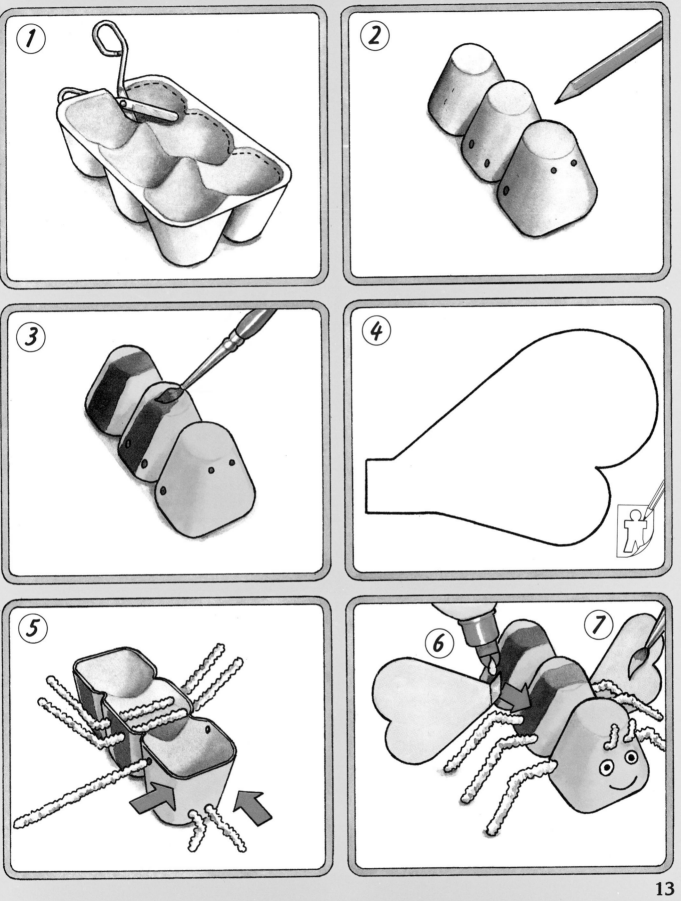

Walking Bird

- A cardboard tube is best for the bird's body. Or you can roll a sheet of cardboard and stick it together.

- Take care when cutting the lengths of yarn so that the bird will balance when complete.

What you need:

① ② ③

Floating Duck

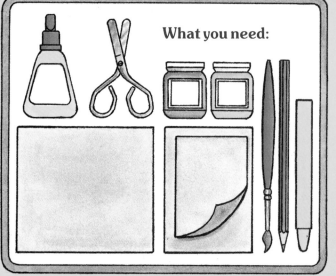

What you need:

- Trace the duck shape in picture 1 onto cardboard. The dotted lines show you where you should fold, the hard lines show where to cut.

- Use a wax crayon or a candle to make the base of the duck waterproof. When you color the duck, use crayon or paint only as far as the waterproofing. Some paints come off in water.

- Use Scotch tape or glue to stick the duck together.

Toilet Roll Dachshund

- A toilet paper roll is best for this project, but you can use a piece of rolled-up cardboard instead. Glue it together or use Scotch tape.

- Trace the outlines in pictures 2, 3, 4 and 5 onto cardboard. You must make 4 legs (picture 5).

- Paint the dog in whatever colors you like. It could have a red nose!

- Try giving it some whiskers made from cotton thread.

- Make a kennel for your dog by cutting a hole in the end of a deep shoe box. Make the roof by gently folding the box lid in half and glue or tape it into position. Paint it in bright colors.

What you need:

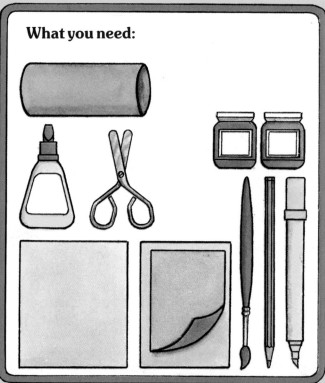

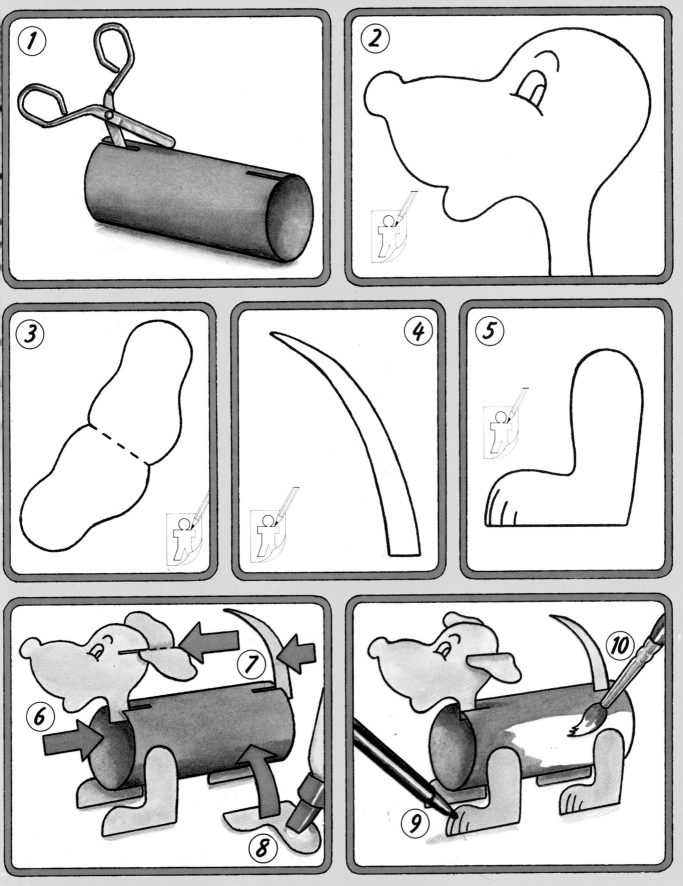

Cardboard Crocodile

- You need a long cardboard tube for this project – the sort of tube you find in the middle of a roll of paper towels. If you do not have one, you can make a tube using cardboard and glue or Scotch tape.

- Make sure the tail and the jaws of the crocodile are long enough.

- Cut the zigzags out of white paper to make the teeth, and glue them into position as shown.

- For the legs, trace the outline in picture 5 four times onto the cardboard.

- Paint the legs before you glue them onto the tube.

What you need:

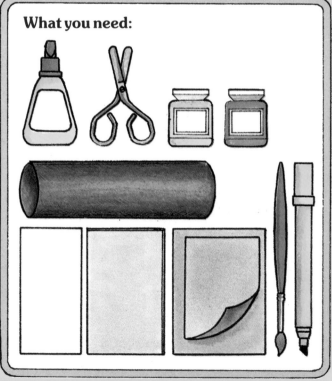

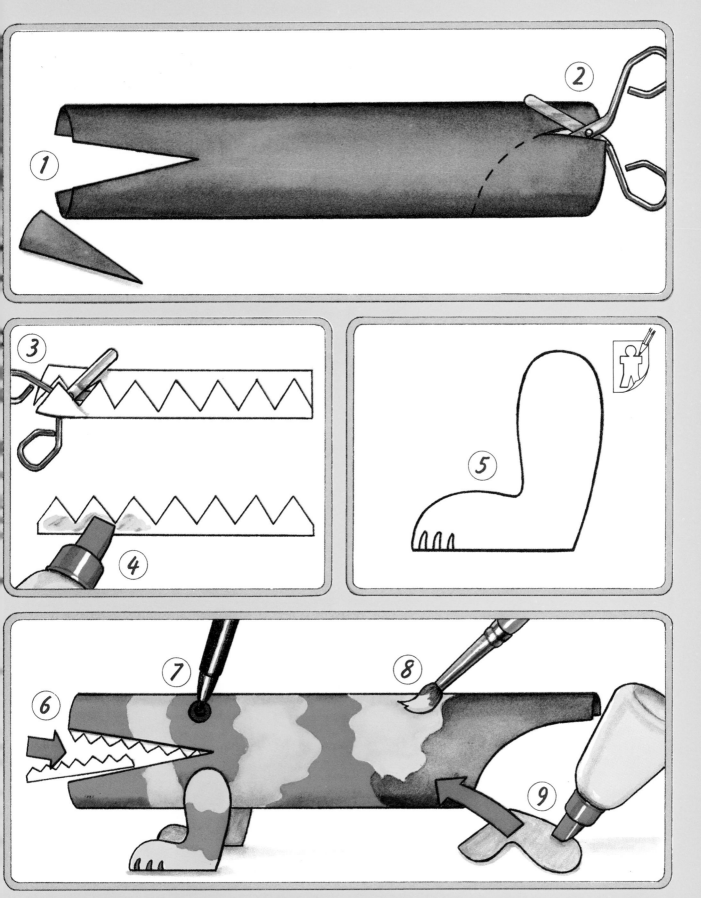

Balancing Bird

- Use stiff cardboard to make this bird.

- Trace the shape in picture 1 very carefully, and be careful, too, when you are cutting it out.

- Position the coins carefully as shown (picture 2), placing them as close to the tips of the wings as possible. You may need to position them by trial and error to get the true balance.

- You can balance the bird on a finger or the edge of a ruler, or even a twig.

- If the bird tilts forward or backward, bend the cardboard gently until it balances properly.

What you need:

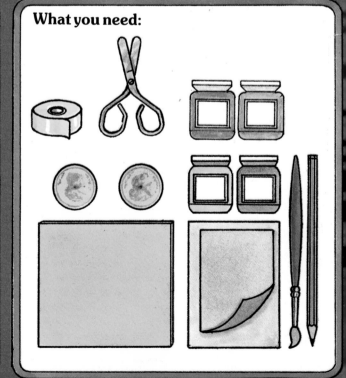

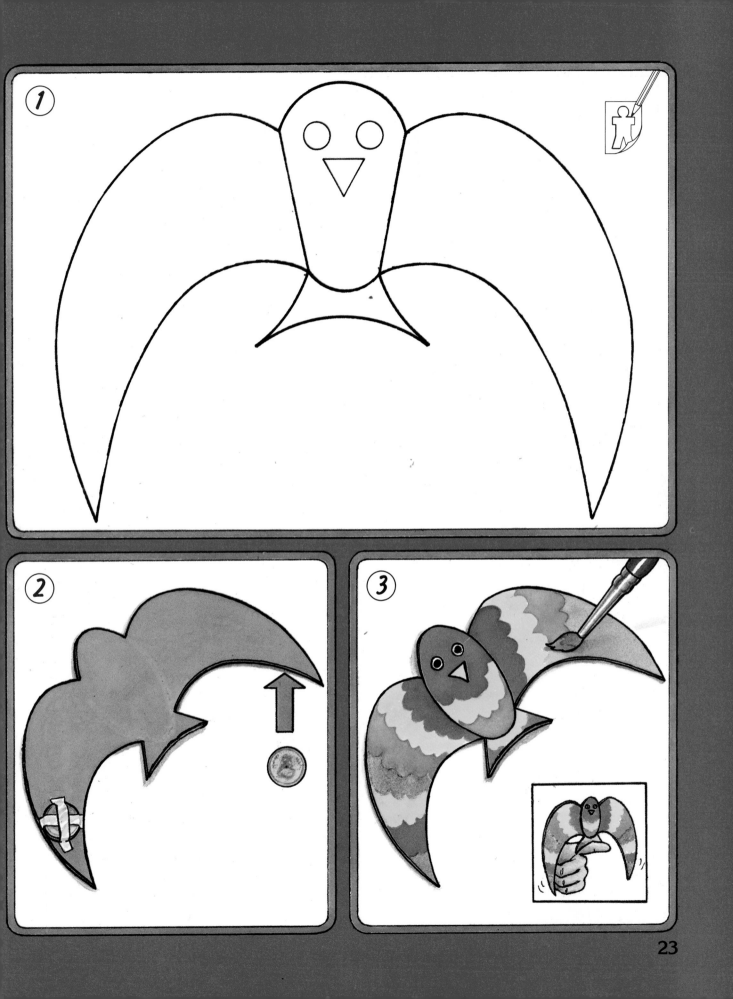

23

Papier Mâché Turtle

- Tear several sheets of newspaper into very small pieces.

- Soak the paper pieces thoroughly before you use them.

- Use a small bowl as a mold. Make sure the paper is completely dry before you take it off the mold.

- Make the legs and tail from modeling clay and line the shell with clay too. Use colored thumbtacks, beads or buttons for the eyes.

What you need:

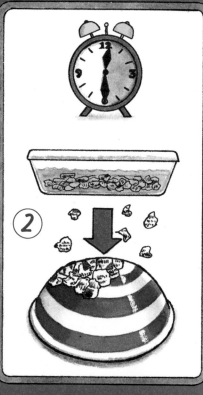

Cork Creepy Crawly

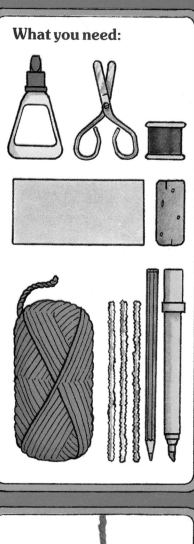

- You can use any kind of yarn, in any color.

- Cut it into small pieces – make sure there is enough yarn to cover the cork.

- You can use colored thumbtacks instead of paper for the eyes. Or glue on small buttons or attach them with pins.

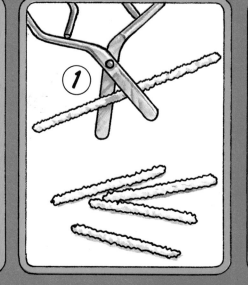

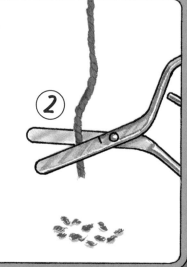

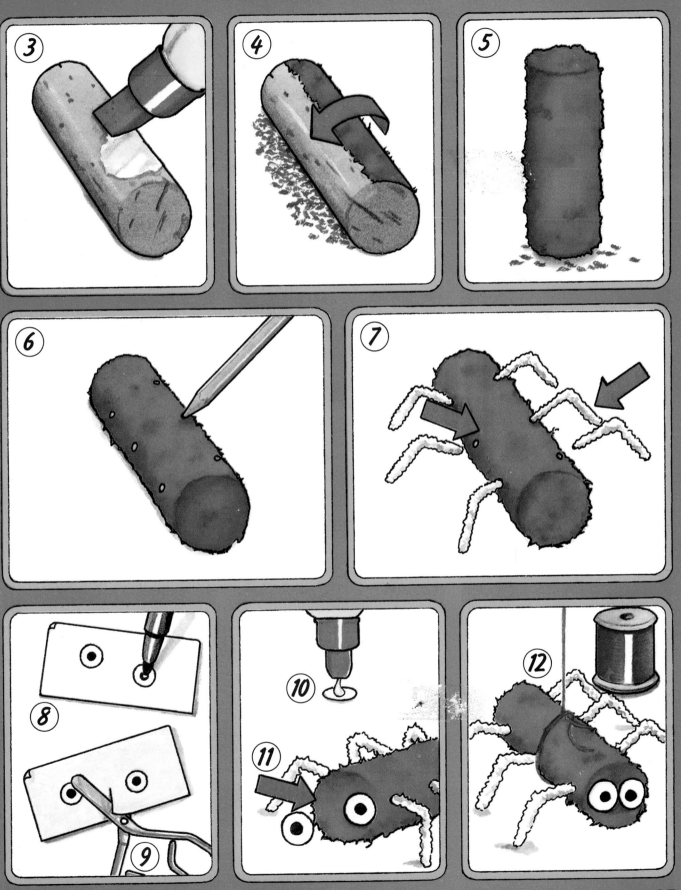

Cardboard Tube Lizard

● You need a long cardboard tube for this project – the sort of tube you find in the middle of a roll of paper towels – or you can make one by rolling a sheet of cardboard and taping it together.

● Draw and cut out the legs and spines as shown in pictures 3 and 6. Remember that the dotted lines show where to make folds.

● Cut out a tongue and roll it as shown in pictures 9 and 10.

What you need:

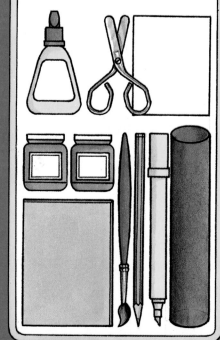

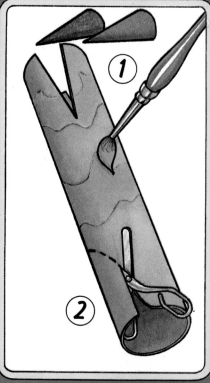

①

②

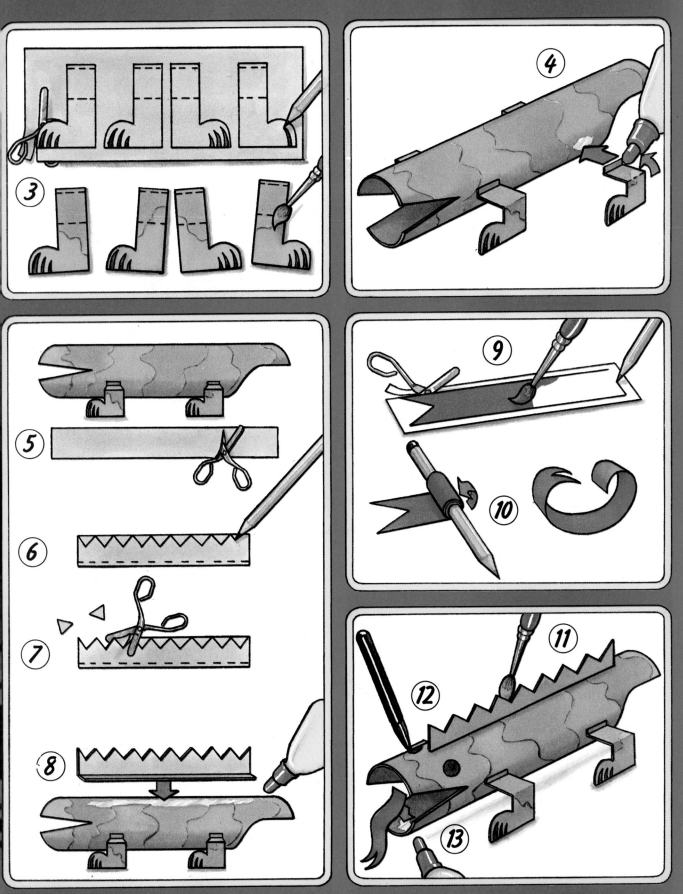

Cardboard Dinosaur

- Fold a sheet of cardboard and trace onto it the outline in picture 1.

- Make sure the spines touch the fold of the cardboard. Do not cut across the top of the two spines.

What you need:

① ② ③

Matchbox Beast

● Draw the neck and head of the beast on the inside tray of the matchbox and watch his neck grow as you push it open.

What you need:

31

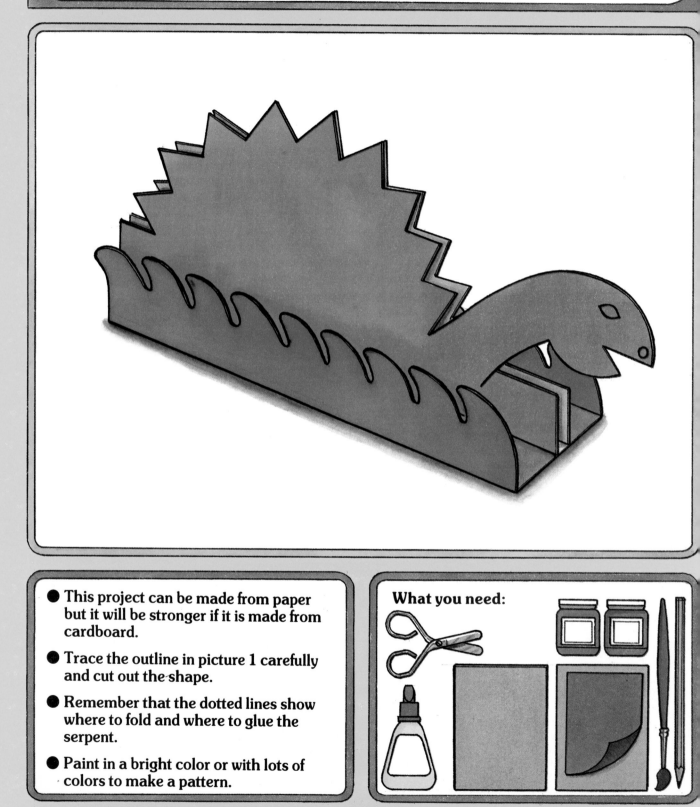

● This project can be made from paper but it will be stronger if it is made from cardboard.

● Trace the outline in picture 1 carefully and cut out the shape.

● Remember that the dotted lines show where to fold and where to glue the serpent.

● Paint in a bright color or with lots of colors to make a pattern.

What you need:

1

2

3

4

5

6

33

Egg Carton Dragon

- Carefully fold in half a piece of cardboard.

- Trace the head onto both sides with the mouth toward the fold.

- When cutting it out do not cut along the fold of the cardboard.

- Use a pipe cleaner or a big needle to thread the string through the egg carton pieces for the body.

- Curl the dragon's tail by winding it around a pencil as shown.

What you need:

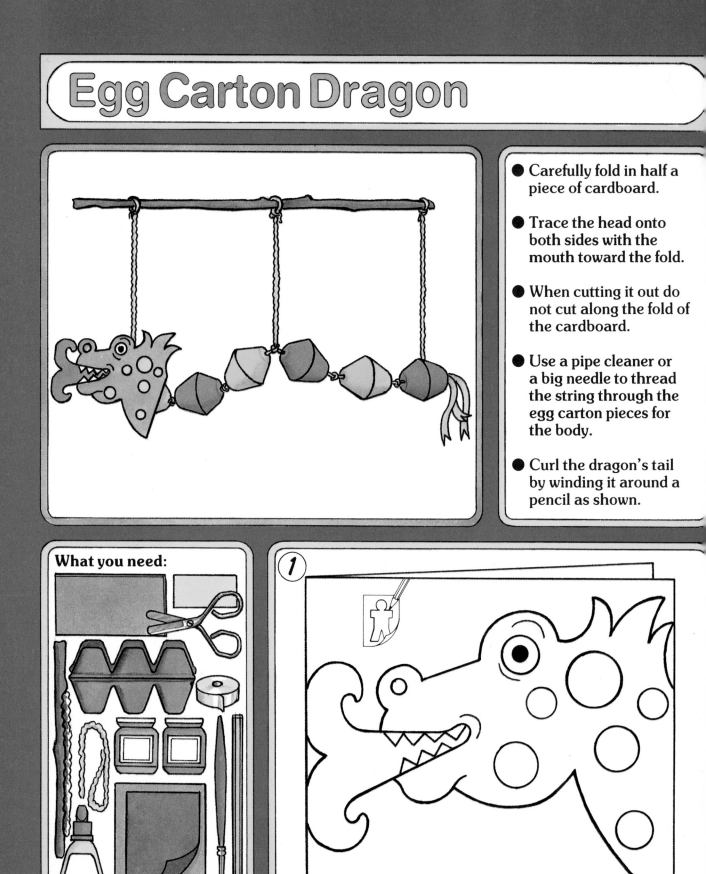

①

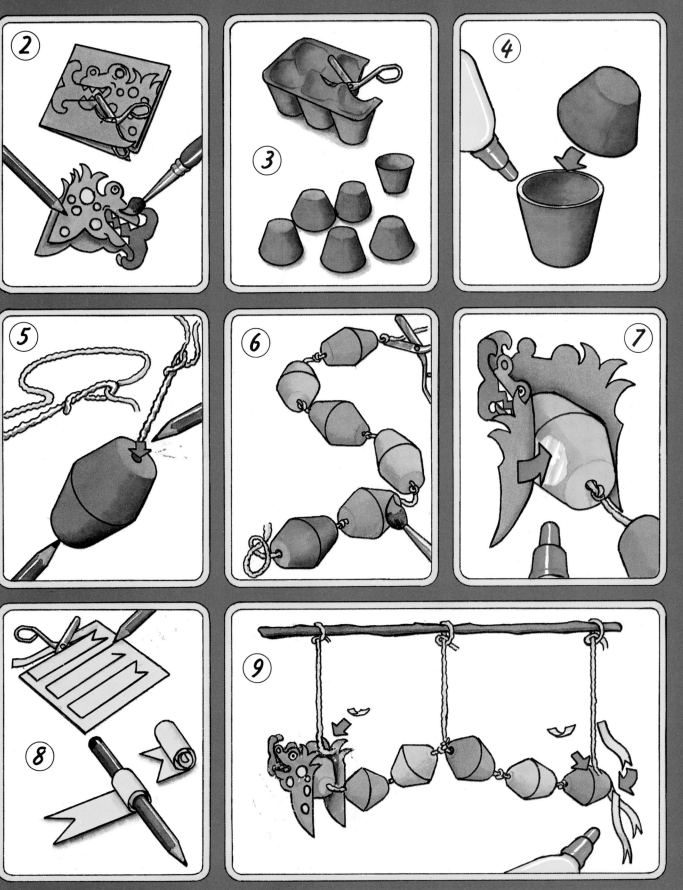

Carton Car

- Small boxes are best for this project – try using a matchbox and a cigarette box.

- Trace four shapes for the wheels, using the outline in picture 2.

- Make a hole in the center of each wheel, and four holes in the larger box. Push pipe cleaners through these holes to make axles.

- Fold over the ends of the pipe cleaners twice to hold the wheels firmly.

What you need:

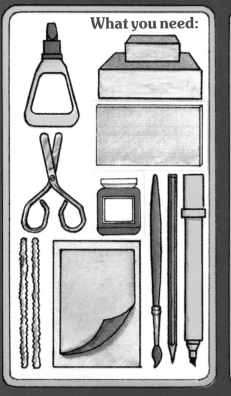

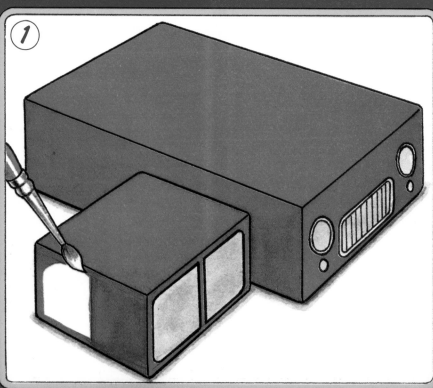

(1)

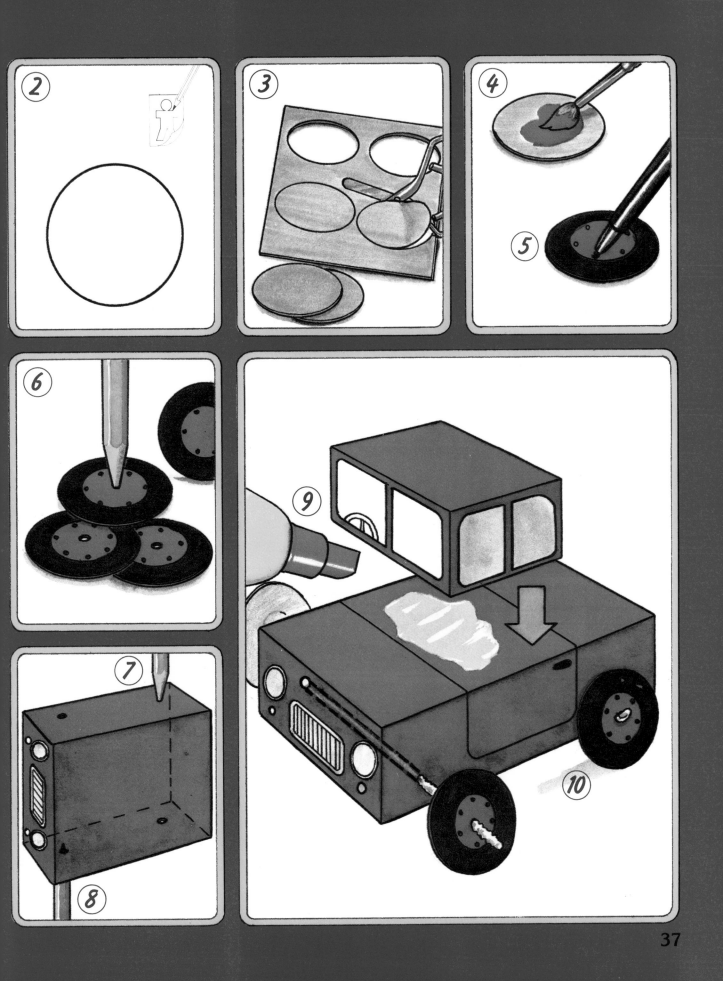

Tanker Trailer

What you need:

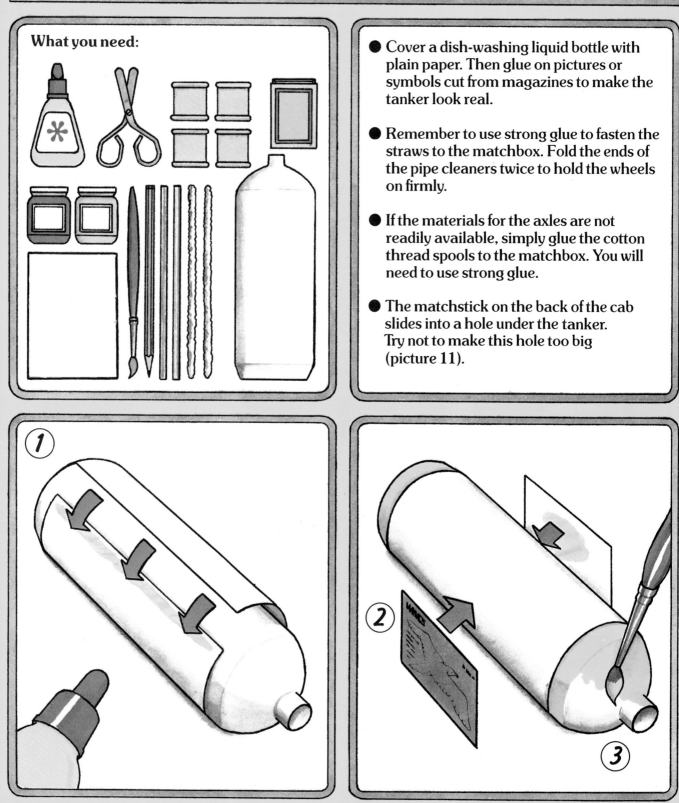

- Cover a dish-washing liquid bottle with plain paper. Then glue on pictures or symbols cut from magazines to make the tanker look real.

- Remember to use strong glue to fasten the straws to the matchbox. Fold the ends of the pipe cleaners twice to hold the wheels on firmly.

- If the materials for the axles are not readily available, simply glue the cotton thread spools to the matchbox. You will need to use strong glue.

- The matchstick on the back of the cab slides into a hole under the tanker. Try not to make this hole too big (picture 11).

Matchbox Train

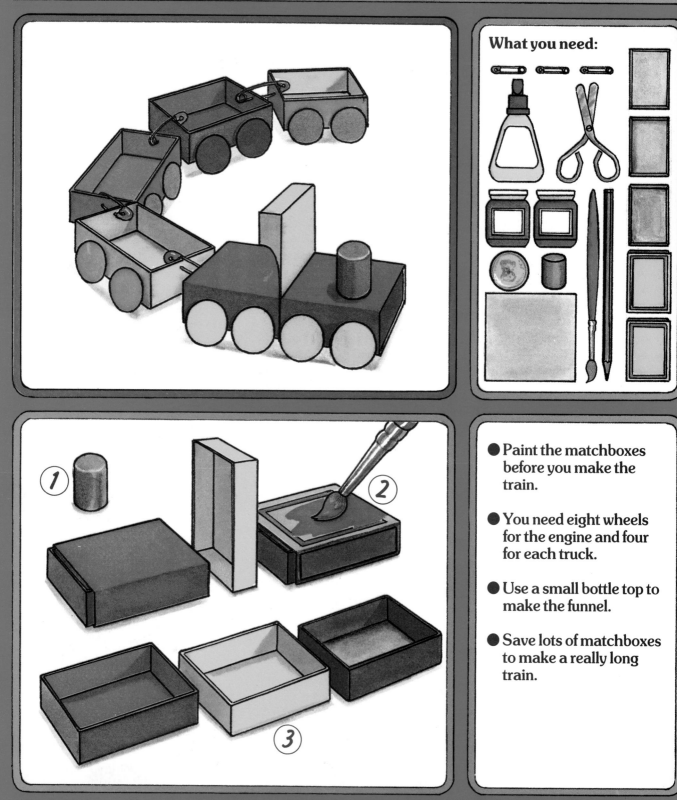

- Paint the matchboxes before you make the train.

- You need eight wheels for the engine and four for each truck.

- Use a small bottle top to make the funnel.

- Save lots of matchboxes to make a really long train.

1

2

3

Balloon Rocket Race

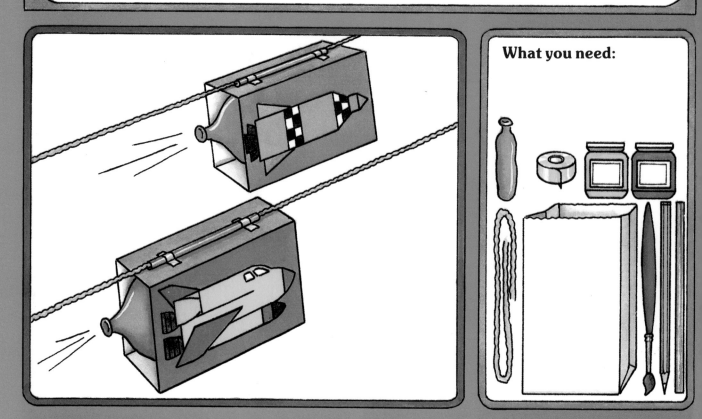

What you need:

- Any strong paper bag will do for this game.

- The balloon must be big enough, when it is blown up, to touch the sides of the bag.

- Fasten a straw onto one side of the bag. Pull enough string or thread through it.

- Suspend the string or thread at an angle between two chairs.

- Blow up the balloon inside the bag and the space rocket blasts off up the string.

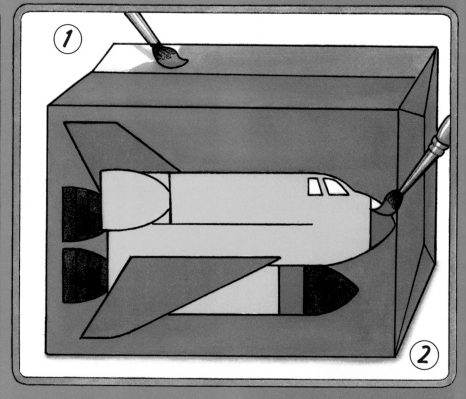

① ②

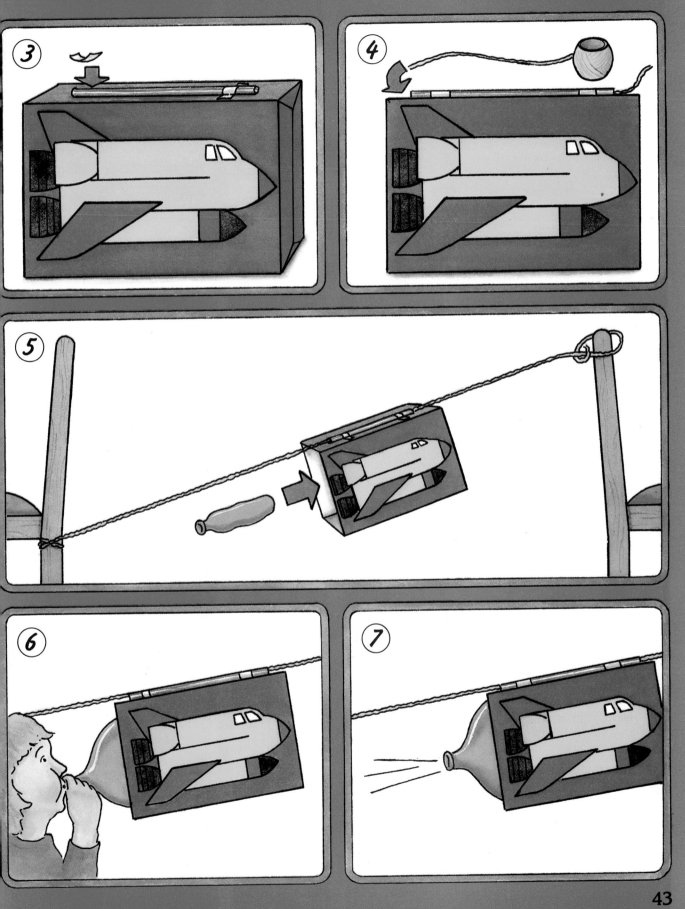

Tanker Cab

- You can make a cab that tilts by using a flip-top cigarette box.

- Use the outline in picture 6 to trace four wheels for the cab. Paint them before you fasten them on.

- Use strong glue to attach the straws to the box.

- Thread pipe cleaners through the straws and the wheels to make axles. Fold the ends over twice to hold the wheels on firmly.

What you need:

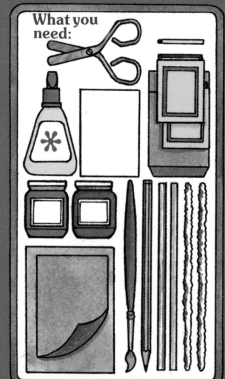

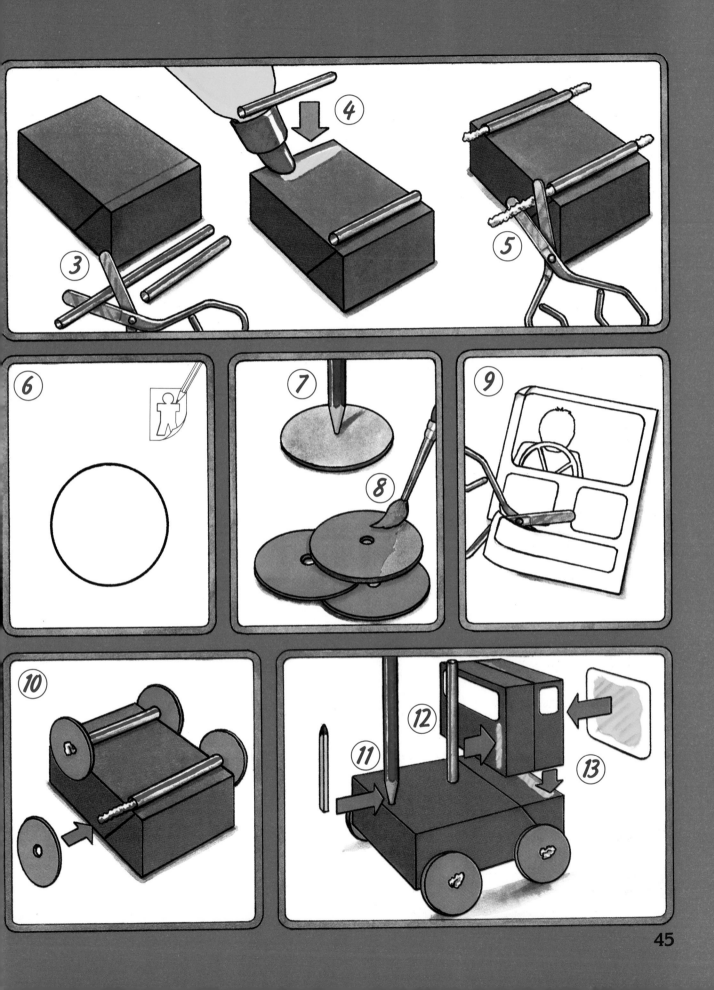

Gas Station

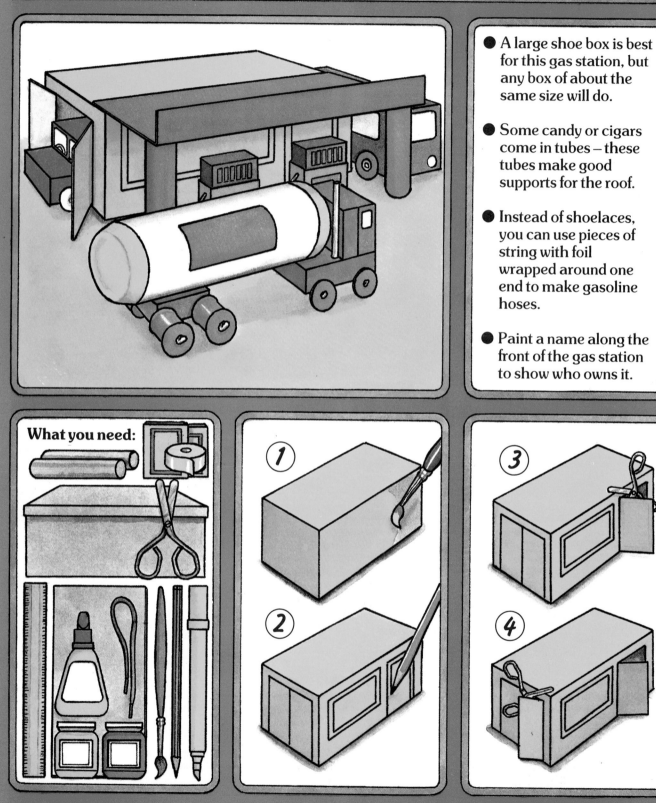

- A large shoe box is best for this gas station, but any box of about the same size will do.

- Some candy or cigars come in tubes – these tubes make good supports for the roof.

- Instead of shoelaces, you can use pieces of string with foil wrapped around one end to make gasoline hoses.

- Paint a name along the front of the gas station to show who owns it.

What you need:

1

2

3

4

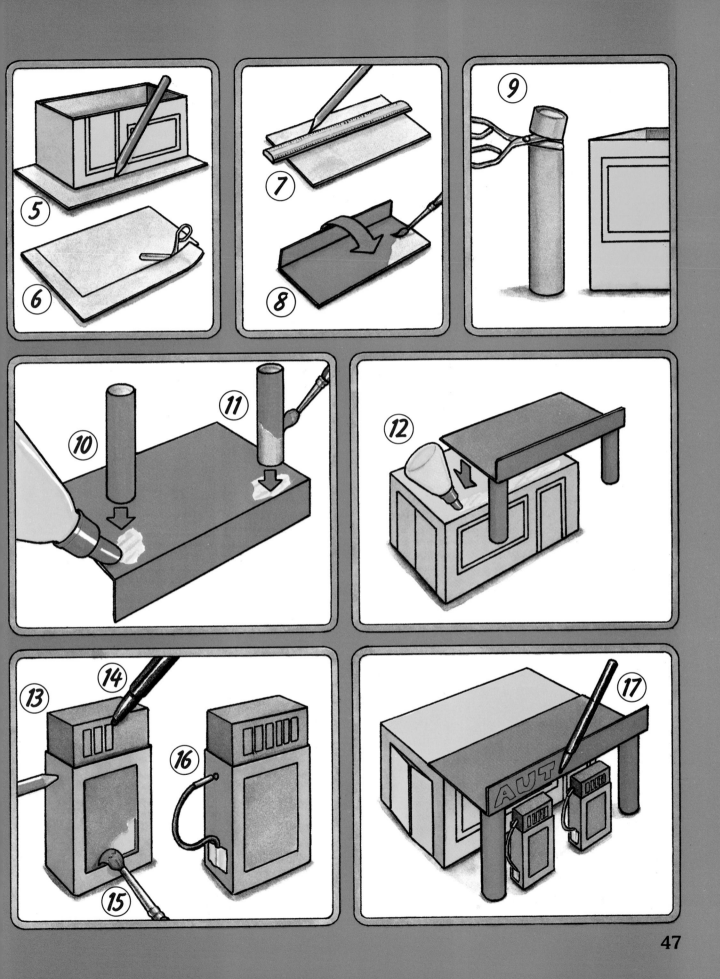

Steamroller

What you need:

- You need strong glue for this project.

- If you do not have a cardboard tube, you can make one using cardboard and Scotch tape.

- A one-pint milk carton is best for this project. Cut off two flaps from the top so that you can seal it neatly.

- If you do not have jar lids for the wheels, you can cut large circles out of thick cardboard instead.

48

Cotton Spool Tank

- Use three small boxes of different sizes – try an individual cereal box, a cigarette box and a matchbox.

- Use either pencils or drinking straws for the axles – but pencils will be stronger.

- Make the tracks from strong paper. Each strip should be at least twice as long as the tank.

- Use modeling clay or glue to attach the cotton spools to the axles.

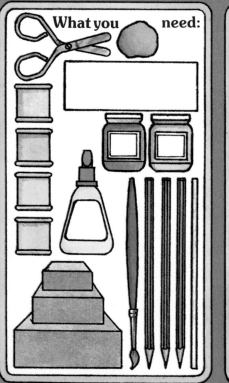

What you need:

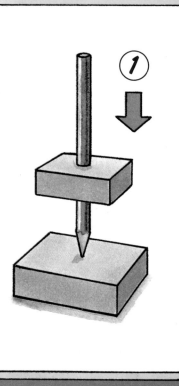

1

2

Milk Carton Bus

What you need:

- Use a large milk carton or a fruit juice carton if you have one.

- Cut off two of the top flaps and seal the carton neatly.

- Trace four wheels onto cardboard, using the outline in picture 4.

- You can use paper clips to hold the wheels instead of pipe cleaners, but they must be fastened on before the carton is sealed.

① ③

②

Viking Longship

What you need:

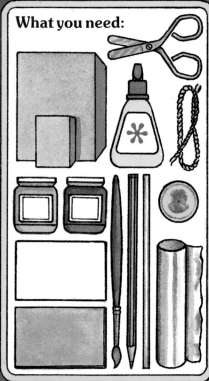

- The best sort of box for this project is a large fruit juice or milk carton.

- You need a smaller box to hold the mast – try a matchbox or a cigarette box.

- Use a strong glue to hold the smaller box in place.

- Shape both ends of the boat using your fingers.

- Or else you can cut a prow shape from cardboard, cover it with foil and attach it with Scotch tape.

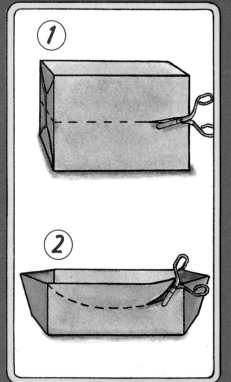

54

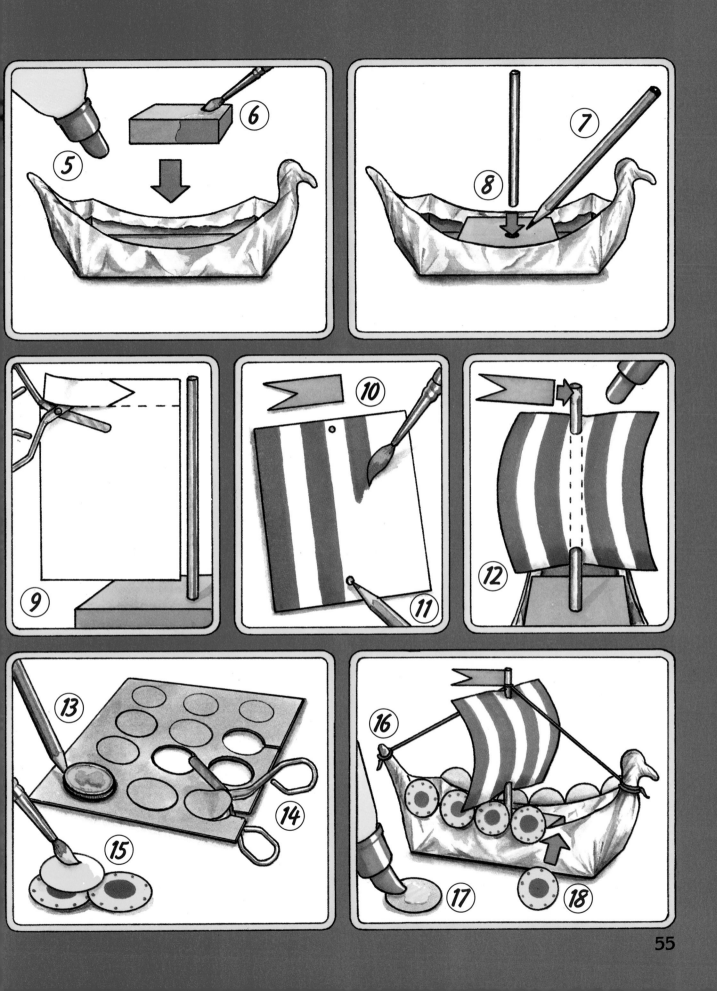

Walnut Boat

- Crack a walnut carefully to get a half shell which is not broken.

- The modeling clay is ballast, to keep the shell steady in the water.

- Make several boats, all with different colored sails. Try racing them by blowing on the sails.

What you need:

1

2

3

4

5

6

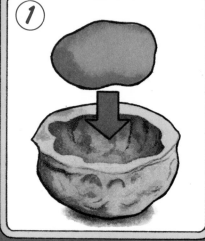

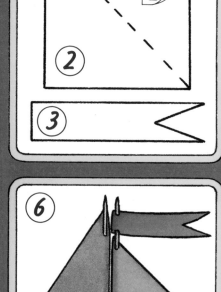

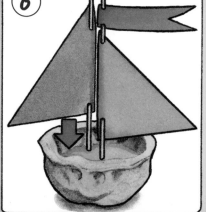

Matchbox Boat

- Use just enough clay to hold the mast and sail straight.

- Curve the sail slightly to help it catch the air as you blow on it.

- Try painting small flags in different colors, and fasten them to the top of the mast.

What you need:

① ② ③ ④ ⑤

Aircraft Carrier

- Cutting the bottle in half is tricky – children will need help.

- The modeling clay is ballast – it keeps the ship steady. But too much will make it too heavy.

- The cardboard for the deck must be large enough to stick out over the edge of the bottle.

- The rubber bands help to hold the ship together and to launch the aircraft.

What you need:

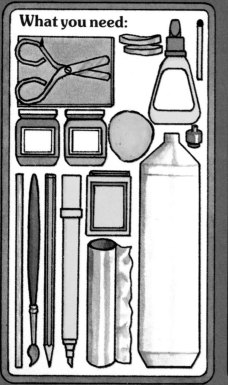

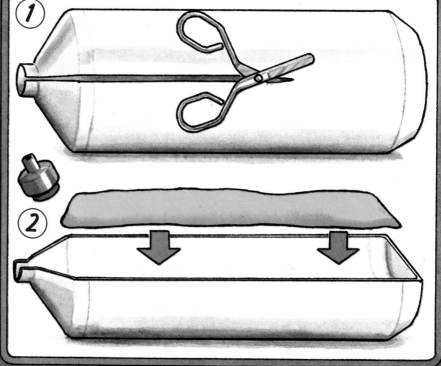

1

2

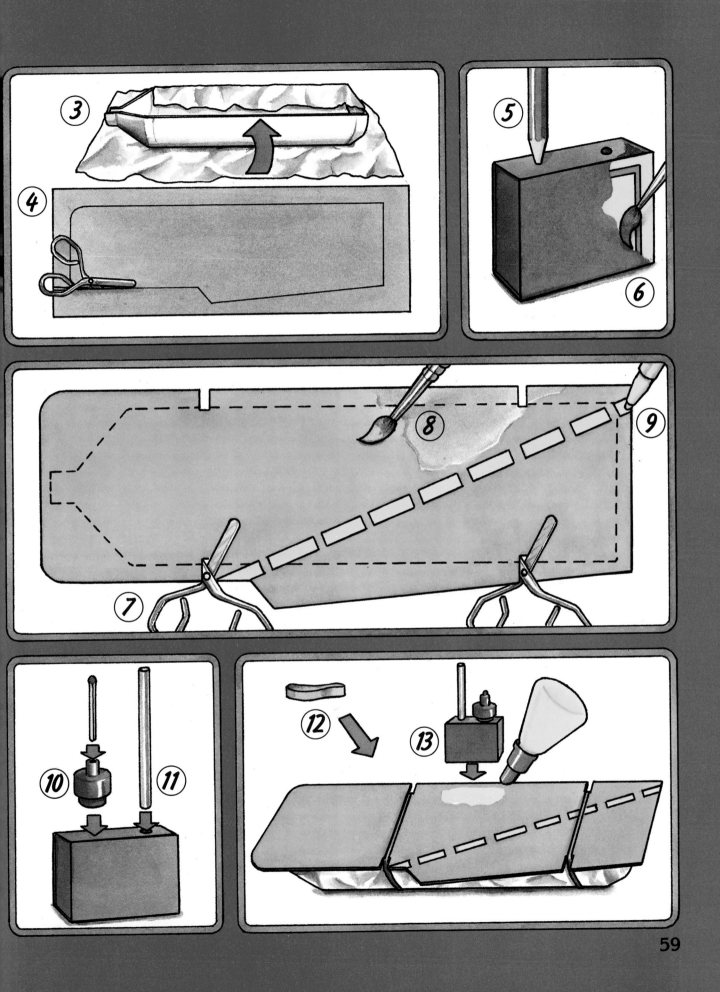

Carton Robot

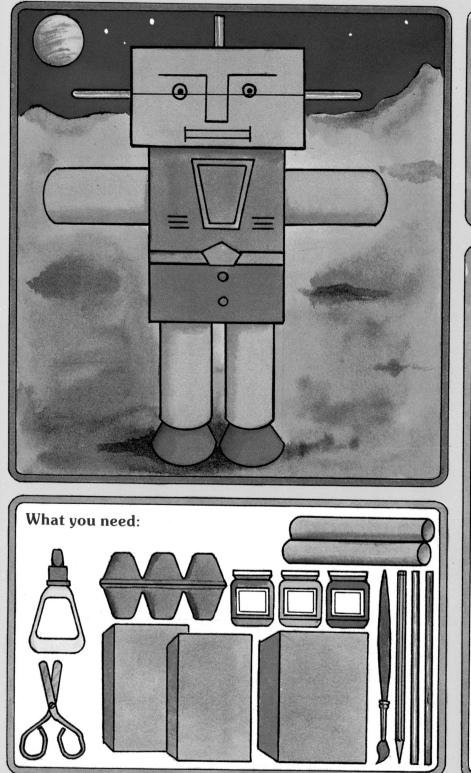

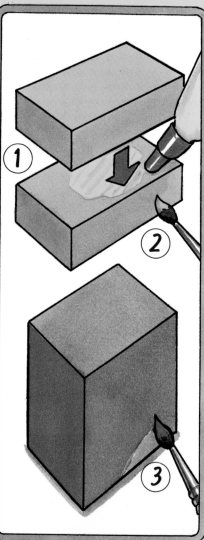

- The robot's head is made with two individual-sized cereal boxes and the body with a small milk or juice carton – but cartons of any size may be used instead.

- You can use cardboard rolled and glued together instead of cardboard tubes.

What you need:

1

2

3

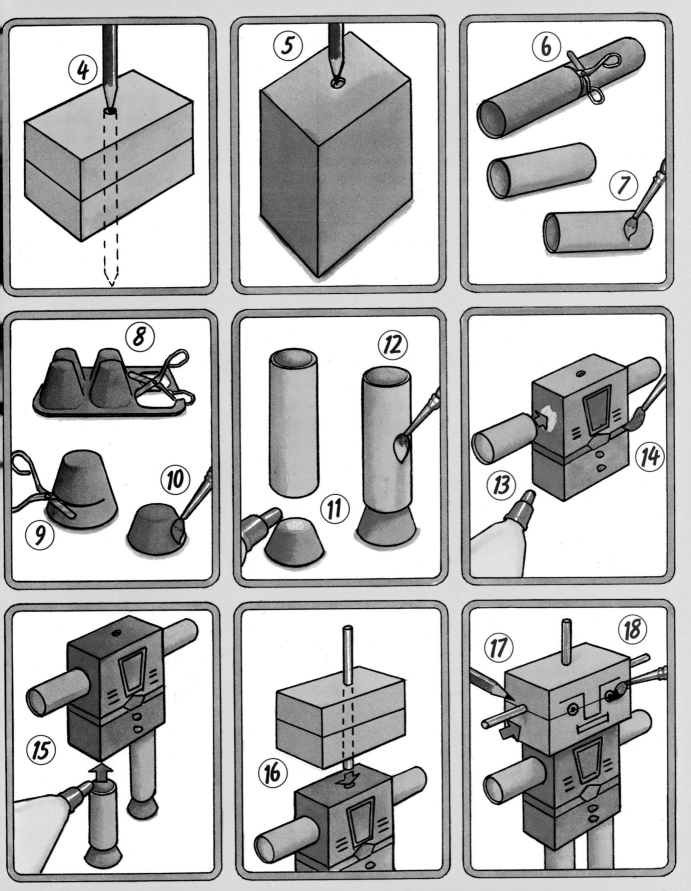

Space Monster

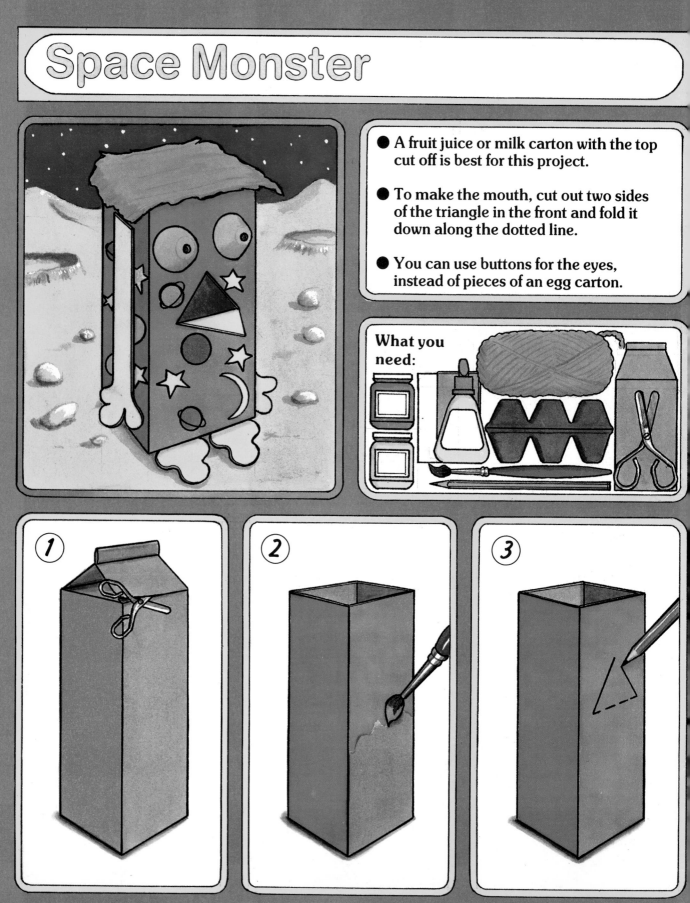

- A fruit juice or milk carton with the top cut off is best for this project.

- To make the mouth, cut out two sides of the triangle in the front and fold it down along the dotted line.

- You can use buttons for the eyes, instead of pieces of an egg carton.

What you need:

1

2

3

63

Cardboard Tube Rocket

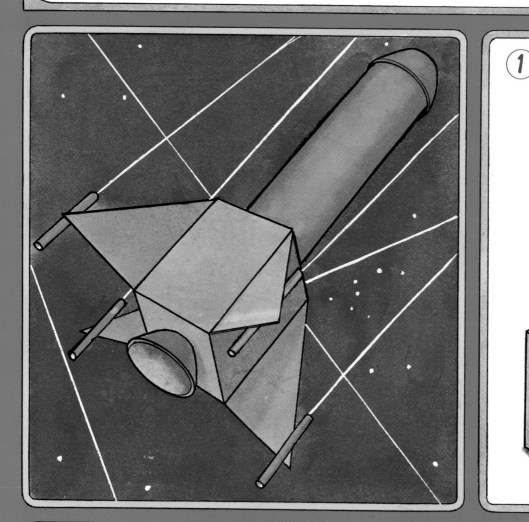

1

- The cardboard tube and carton can be of any size as long as the proportions are approximately as illustrated.

- Cut the wings carefully to size so that they fit neatly onto the carton.

- You can use toothpicks or matchsticks for the laser guns instead of drinking straws, if necessary.

What you need:

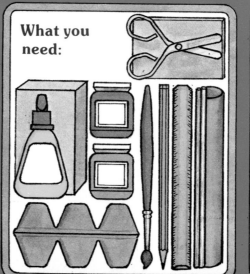

2

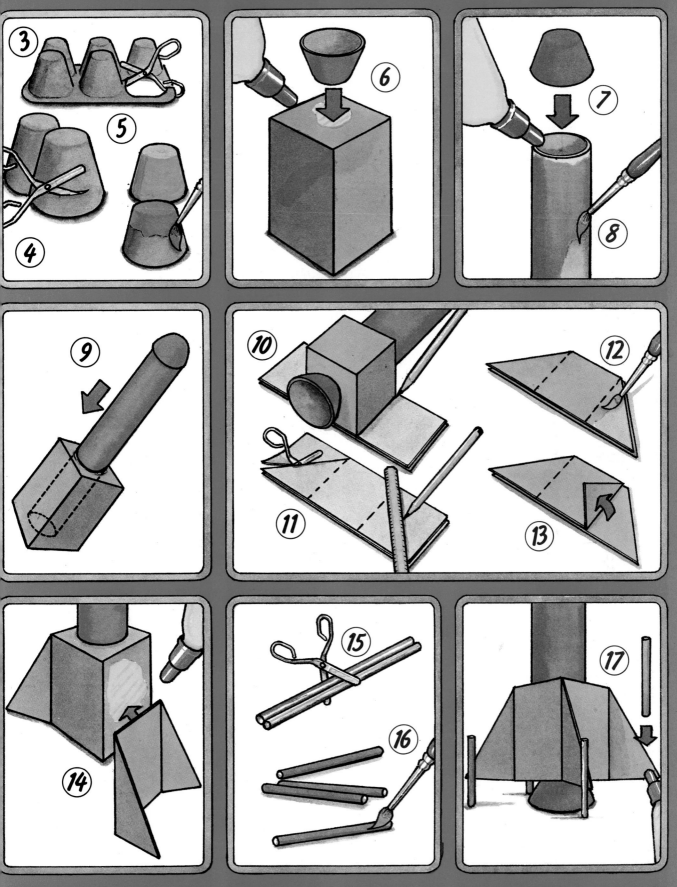

Yogurt Container Satellite

- A small yogurt or cottage cheese container is best for this project, but it should have a lid.

- Trace the outline in picture 5 twice to make the solar panels.

- A container of any size will do but the size of the silver solar panels will need to change to fit it.

- If you have no lid for the container, cut a circle of cardboard to size, scotch tape it into position, and paint it.

What you need:

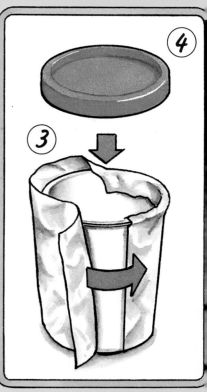

Egg Carton Moon Buggy

- You need 2 egg cartons for this project.

- Use thick cardboard to make the steering wheel and dashboard.

- If you do not wish to use eggs, you can model the astronauts from modeling clay and paint them.

- Cut circles out of thick cardboard for the wheels if you do not have cotton thread spools.

What you need:

1

2

3

4

5

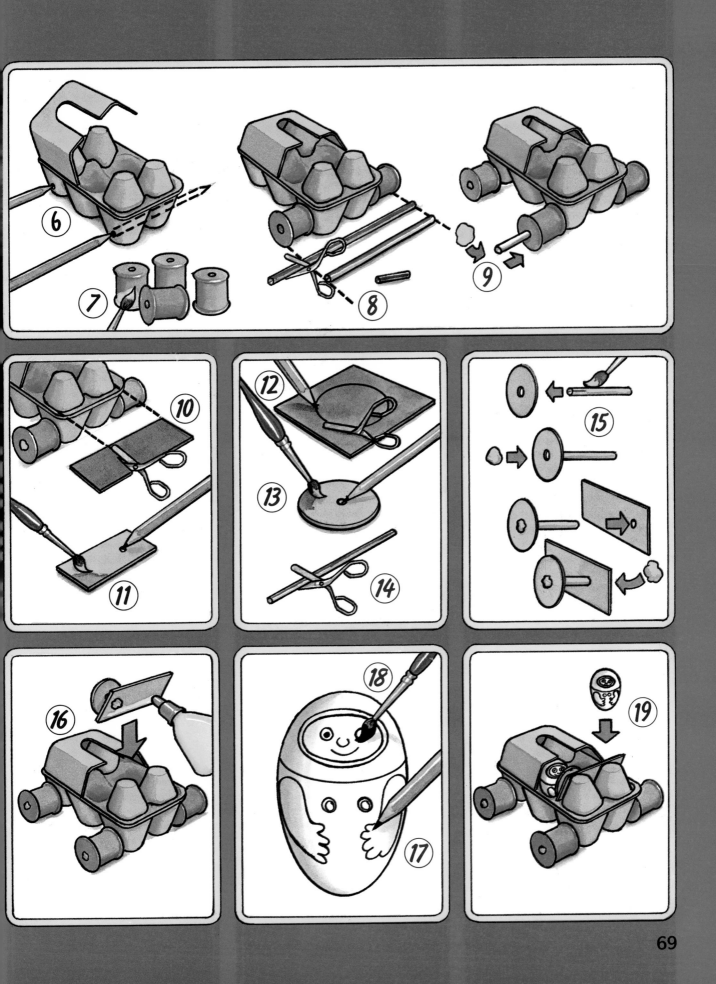

Cardboard Flying Saucer

- Two paper plates glued together are ideal for this project but a plate-sized circle of cardboard will work, too.

- Paper or plastic cups cut to size may be used instead of a yogurt container if necessary.

- Hook the loop of the rubber band around the nick in the flying saucer. Hold the saucer firmly near the nick and stretch the rubber band. Let go of the saucer and it will spin through the air.

What you need:

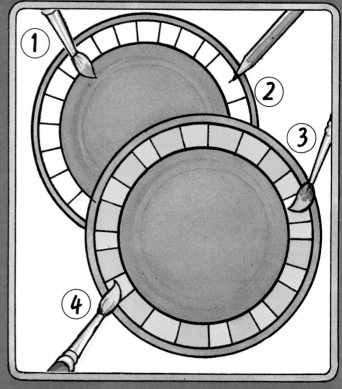

Cardboard Biplane

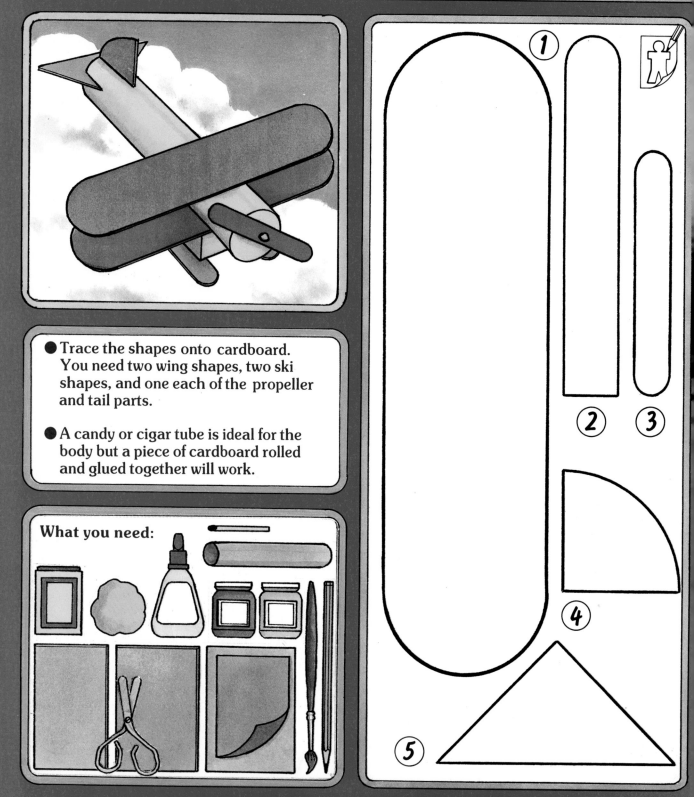

● Trace the shapes onto cardboard. You need two wing shapes, two ski shapes, and one each of the propeller and tail parts.

● A candy or cigar tube is ideal for the body but a piece of cardboard rolled and glued together will work.

What you need:

① ② ③ ④ ⑤

72

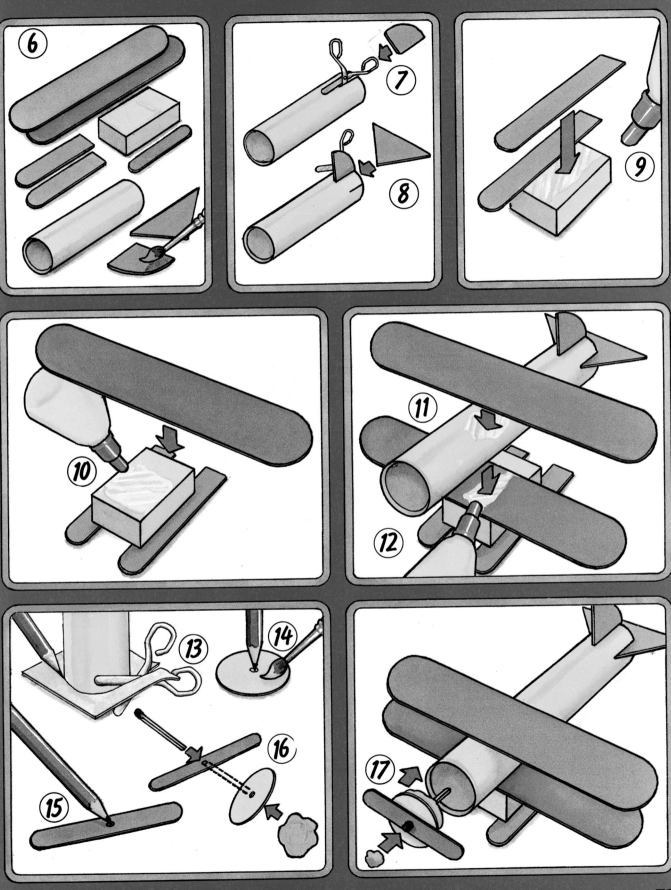

Potato Helicopter

- Children may need help in cutting the potato in half.

- Cut a piece of cardboard for the tail the same length as the potato, and make the hole in the end of it large enough to fit a drinking straw.

- Small candy or cigar tubes will make ideal floats for a large potato helicopter, but you can roll sheets of cardboard and glue them together to make tubes of a size suitable for your potato.

What you need:

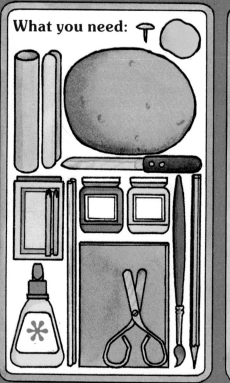

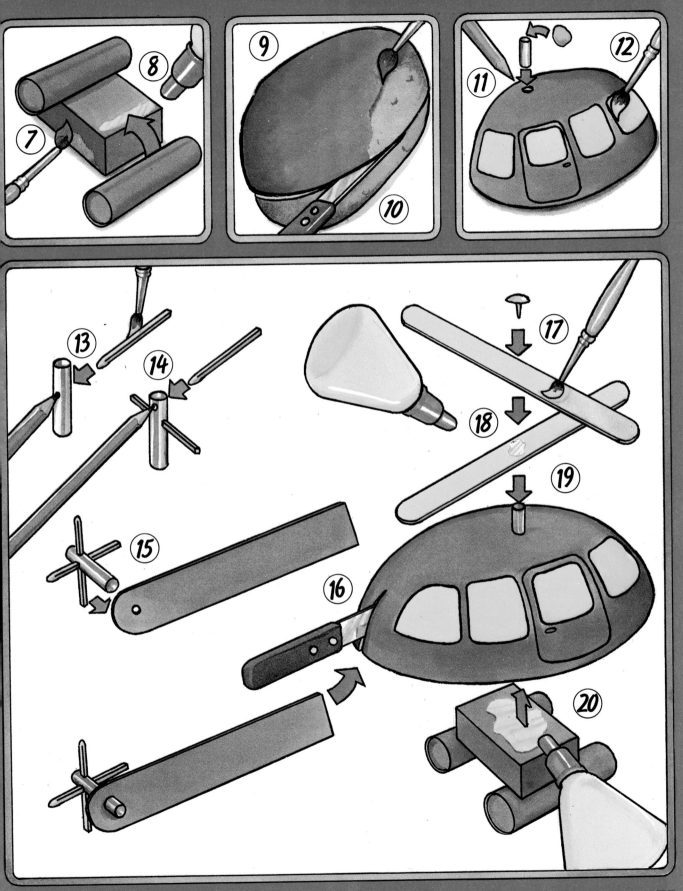

Parachute Game

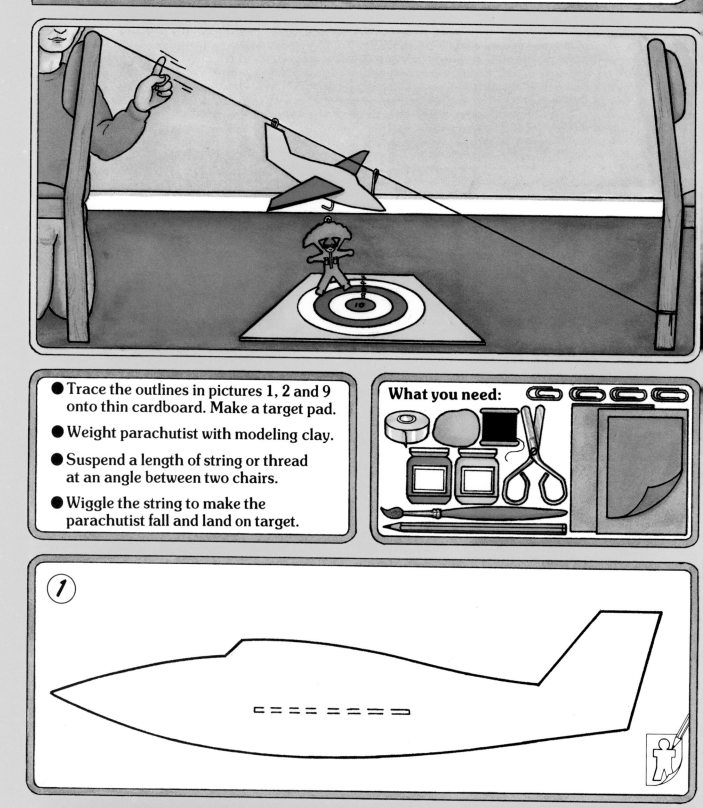

- Trace the outlines in pictures 1, 2 and 9 onto thin cardboard. Make a target pad.

- Weight parachutist with modeling clay.

- Suspend a length of string or thread at an angle between two chairs.

- Wiggle the string to make the parachutist fall and land on target.

What you need:

1

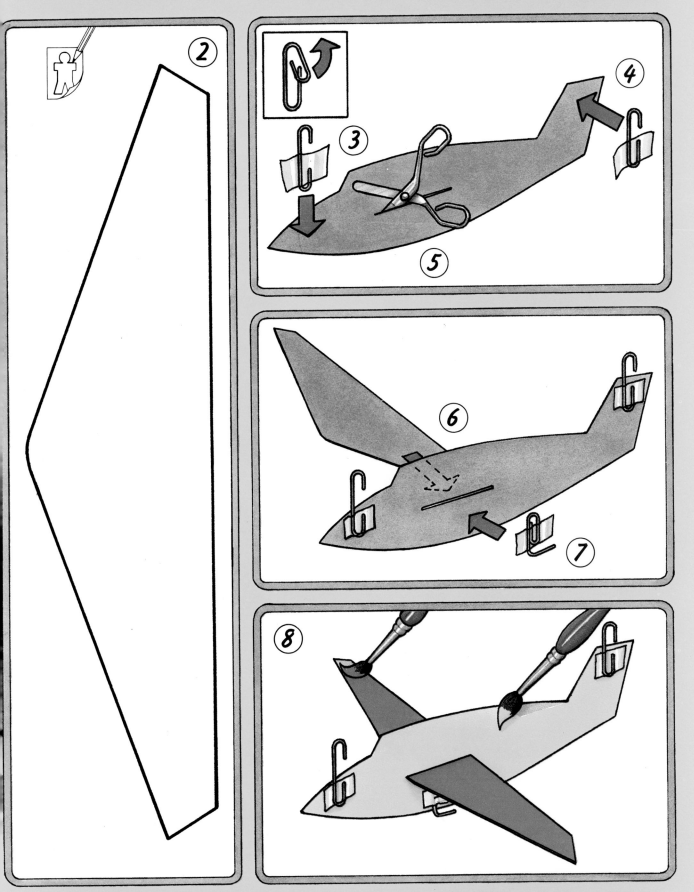

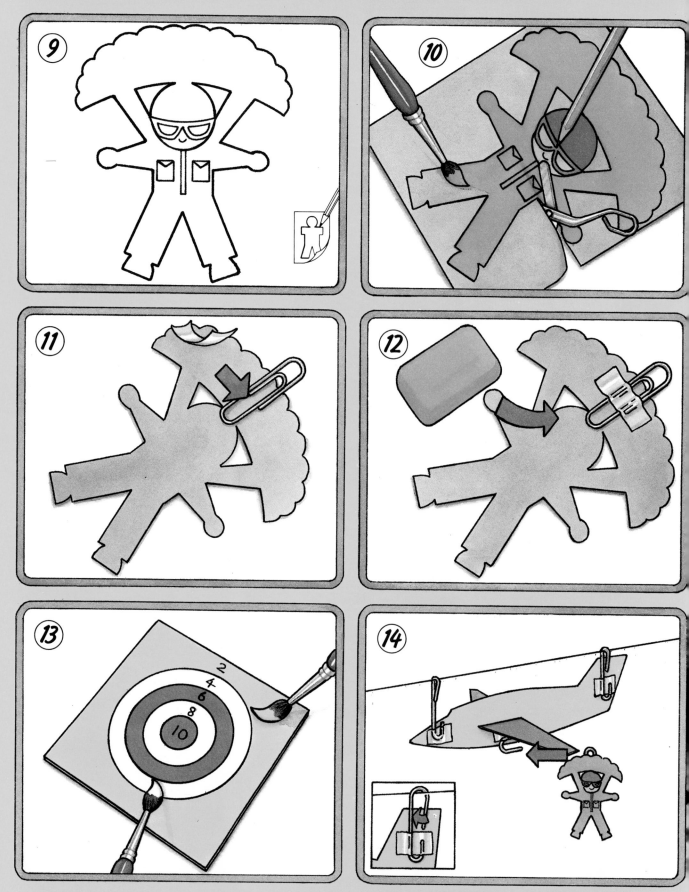

Snap Card Game

- Cut out pictures of people from magazines.
- Play like Snap. Call out when the card before or after your own comes from the same picture.

What you need:

1
2
3
4
5
6

Animal Misfit Cards

- Trace the fox, monkey, alligator and dolphin onto paper. Think of other animals, too.
- Paint the animals and glue them to thick cardboard. Then cut them into 3.
- Now you can create some very unusual beasts!

What you need:

⑦

⑧

Humpty Plate Puppet

- Two paper plates are ideal, but you can make circles by drawing around a plate and cutting them out.
- Trace the nose and bow tie from picture 1.
- Use pipe cleaners, clay and corks for the arms and legs.

What you need:

1
2
3

82

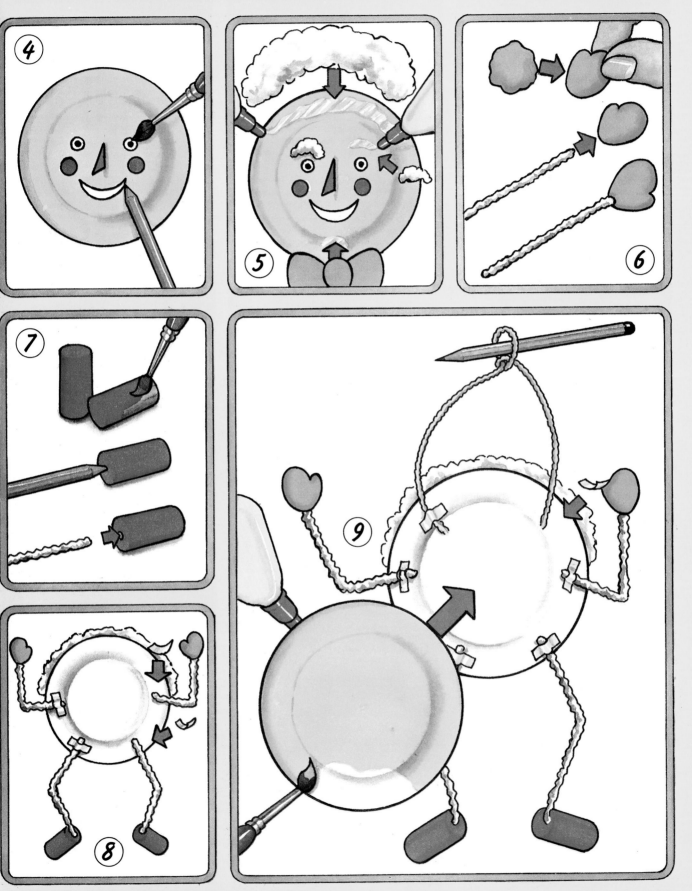

Stick Clown

- Mix flour and water to make the paste into which strips of newspaper are dipped.

- Make sure that the papier mâché is completely dry before bursting the balloon inside it.

- You may need to secure the head to the stick with plasticine or glue.

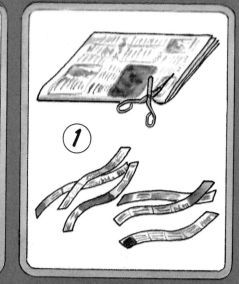

84

Sock Muppet

What you need:

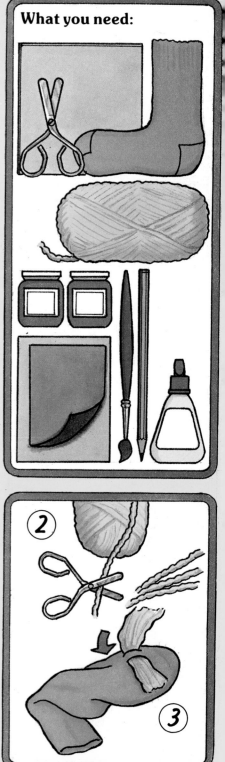

- Use any old sock or a thick stocking cut to size for this project.

- Be sure to make the cut – picture 1 – on the top of the foot of the sock.

- Trace the eyes from the outline in picture 5. Trace the mouth from the outline in picture 7.

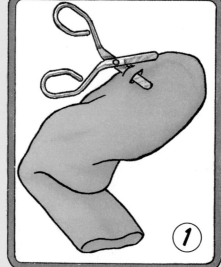

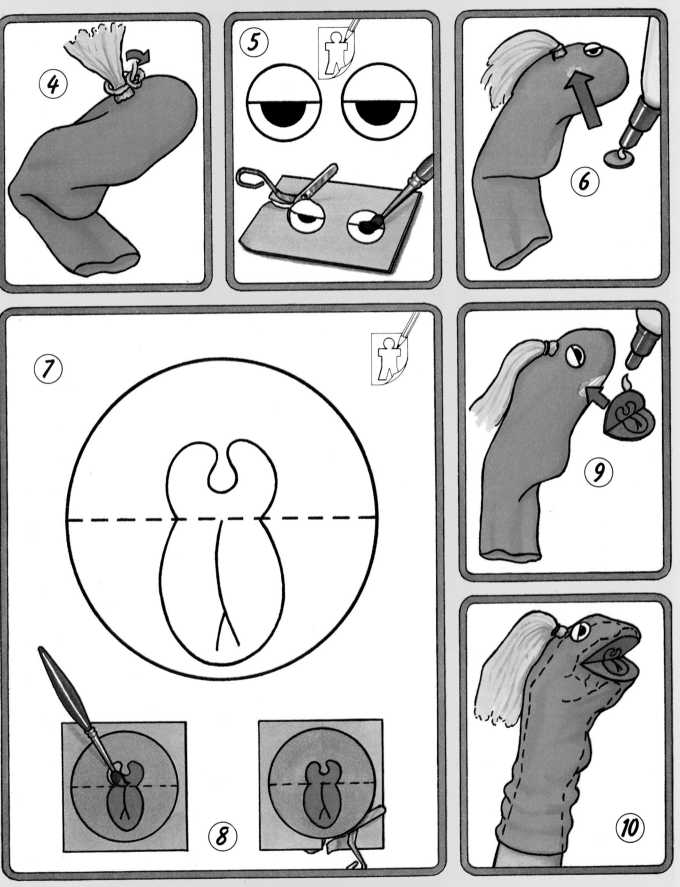

Party Invitation Pop-up

- Trace the outline in picture 1 onto thin cardboard.

- Cut around the solid outline of the clown carefully, pushing the scissors through the card to start. Do not cut the dotted lines as they show you where to fold.

- Write your message in the space below the wall.

What you need:

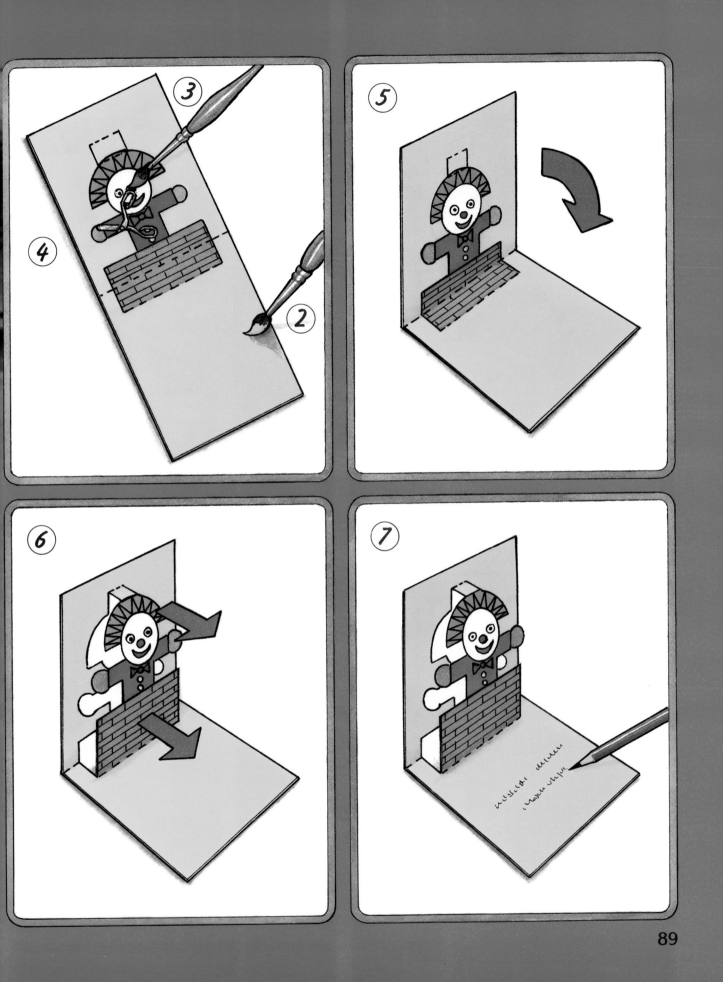

Napkin Rings

- If you do not have a cardboard tube you can make your own by rolling cardboard and glueing it.

- The rings can be painted or covered with colored or aluminum foil.

- You can cut out any design to decorate the rings. Your friends will know where to sit if you put their names on the rings.

What you need:

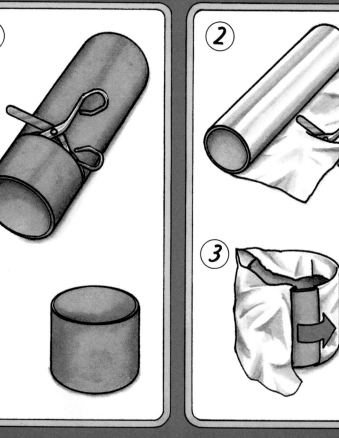

① ② ③

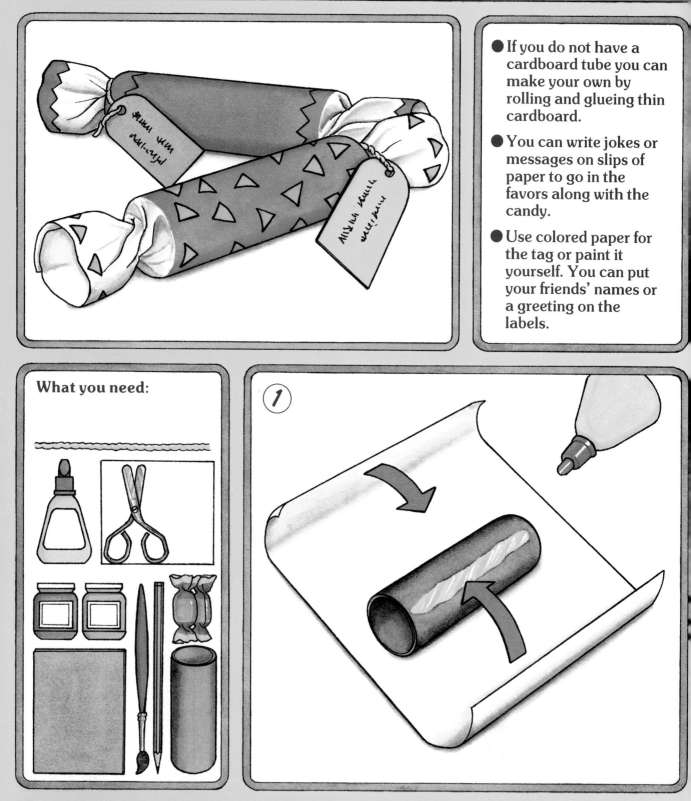

- If you do not have a cardboard tube you can make your own by rolling and glueing thin cardboard.

- You can write jokes or messages on slips of paper to go in the favors along with the candy.

- Use colored paper for the tag or paint it yourself. You can put your friends' names or a greeting on the labels.

What you need:

①

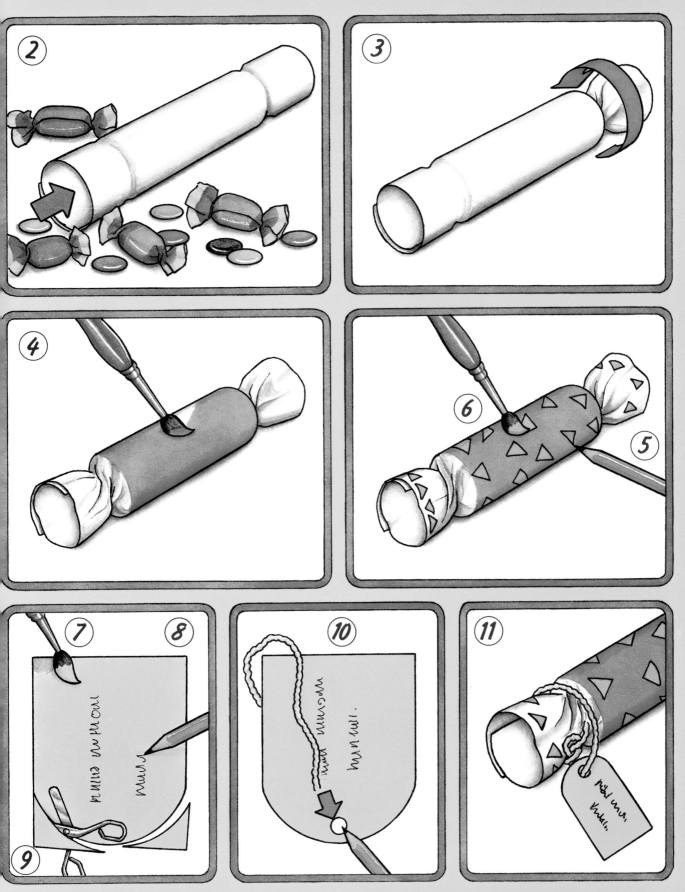

Decorated Eggs

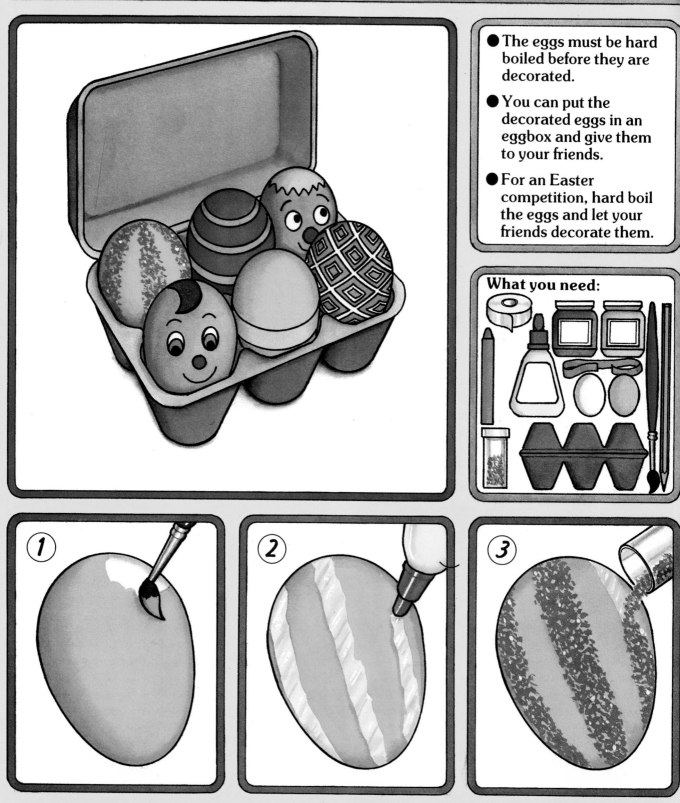

- The eggs must be hard boiled before they are decorated.

- You can put the decorated eggs in an eggbox and give them to your friends.

- For an Easter competition, hard boil the eggs and let your friends decorate them.

What you need:

① ② ③

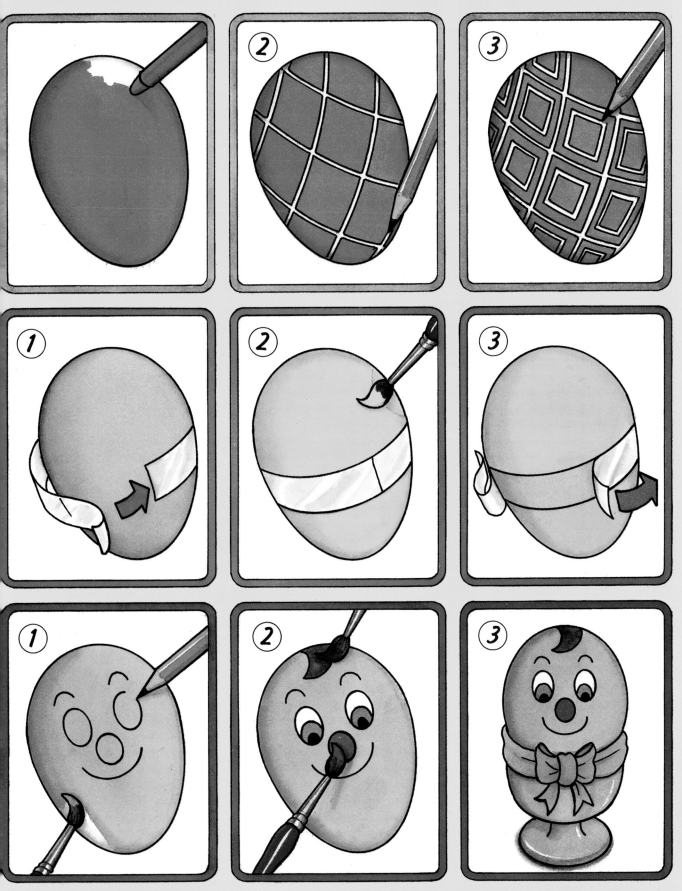

95

Party Presents

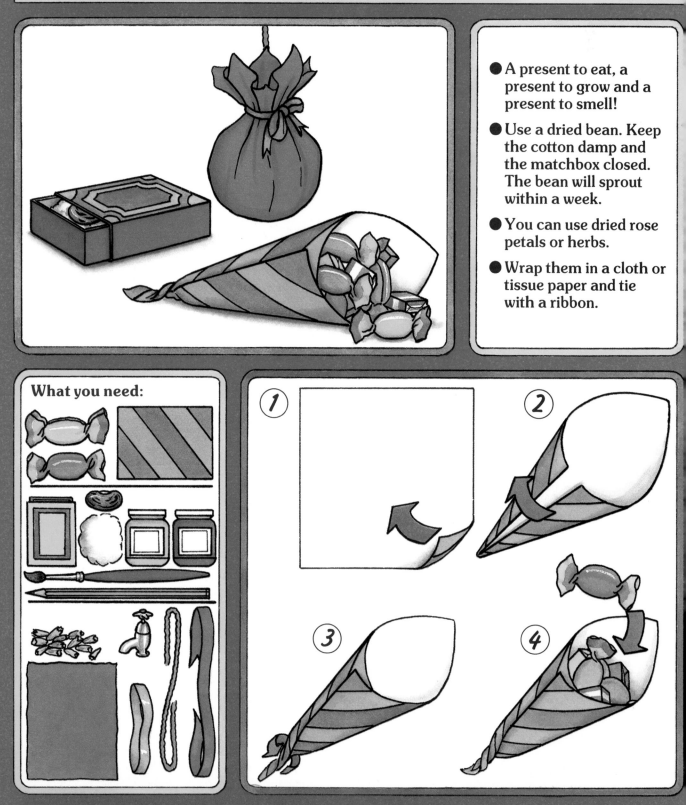

- A present to eat, a present to grow and a present to smell!

- Use a dried bean. Keep the cotton damp and the matchbox closed. The bean will sprout within a week.

- You can use dried rose petals or herbs.

- Wrap them in a cloth or tissue paper and tie with a ribbon.

What you need:

1
2
3
4

Party Hats

- Make sure the hat is going to fit before you glue it together.
- You can copy the pirate's hat or make your own.
- Cut the notches in the base of the top hat from the center to the fold line.

What you need:

1
2
3
4
5

98

Werewolf Mask

- Draw around a plate to make the circle and add the ears before cutting it out.
- Copy the werewolf design and press out holes for the eyes.
- Cut around the heavy line of the nose and fold it back along the dotted line.
- Follow pictures 8, 9 and 10 for the fingernails.

What you need:

1

2

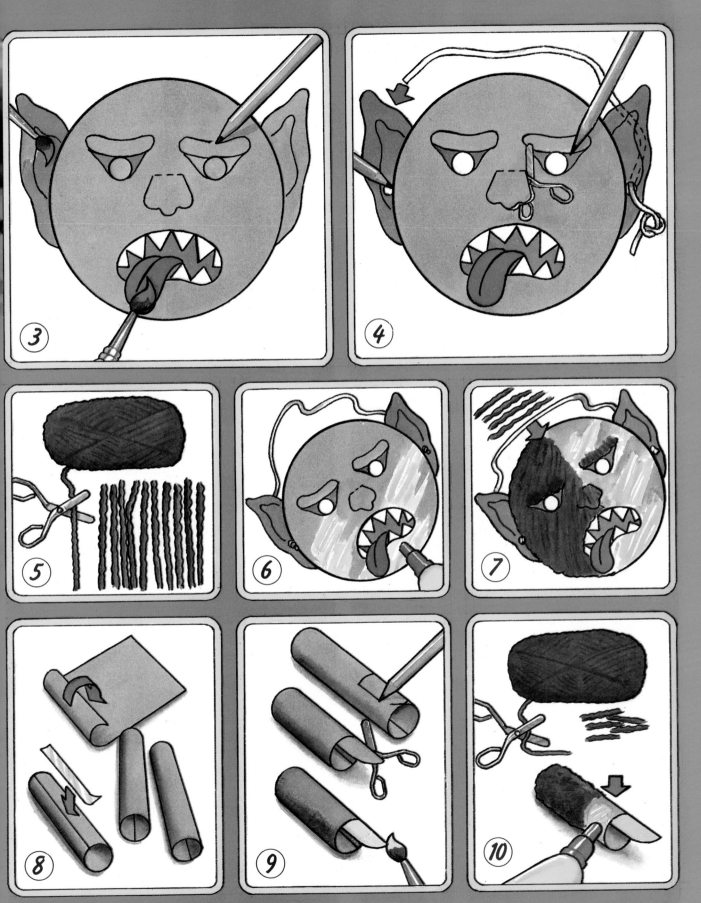

Clown Mask

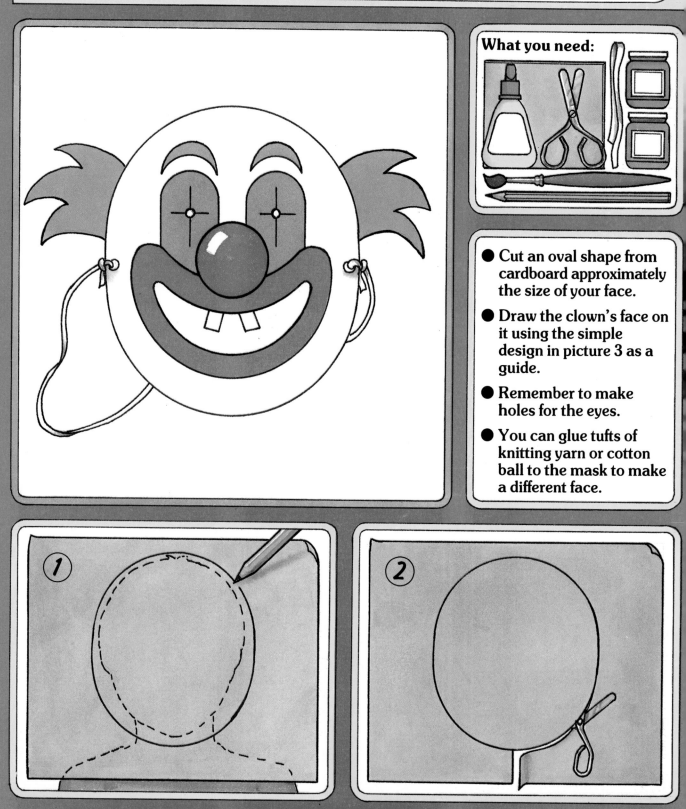

What you need:

- Cut an oval shape from cardboard approximately the size of your face.

- Draw the clown's face on it using the simple design in picture 3 as a guide.

- Remember to make holes for the eyes.

- You can glue tufts of knitting yarn or cotton ball to the mask to make a different face.

① ②

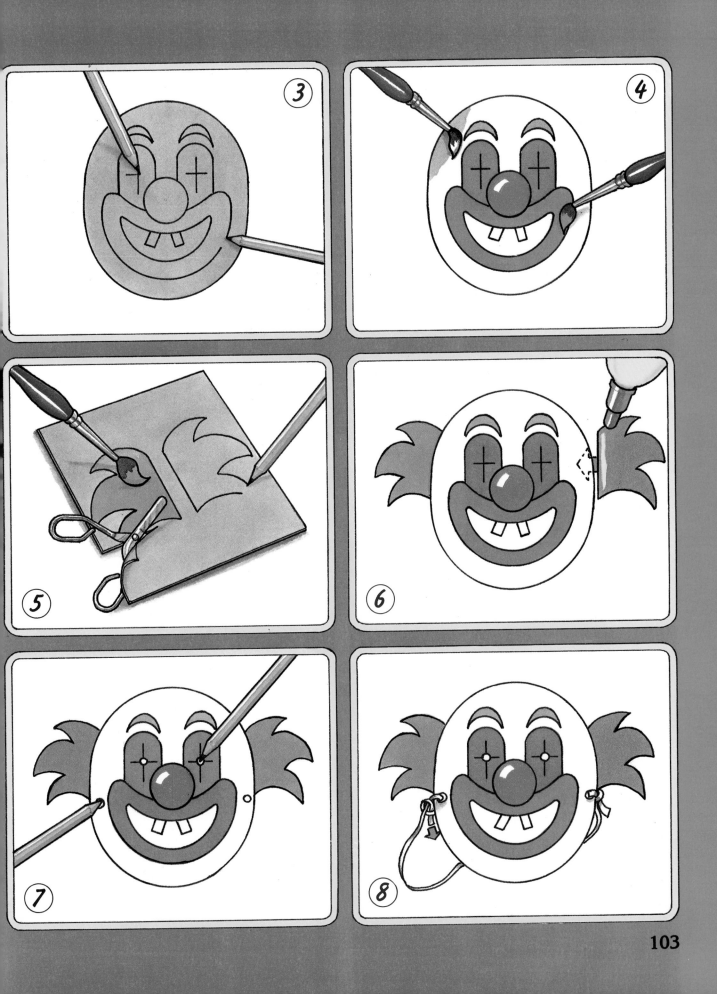

Party Masks

- Trace off the pirate's eyepatch in picture 1 and the cat mask in picture 7.

- Tie strings through holes punched in the sides of the eyepatch and mask.

What you need:

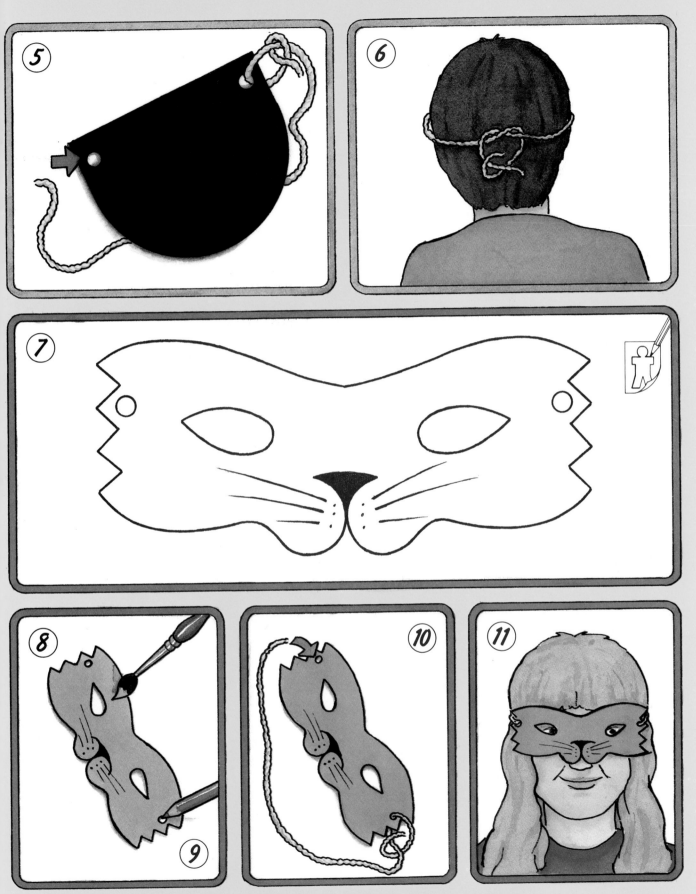

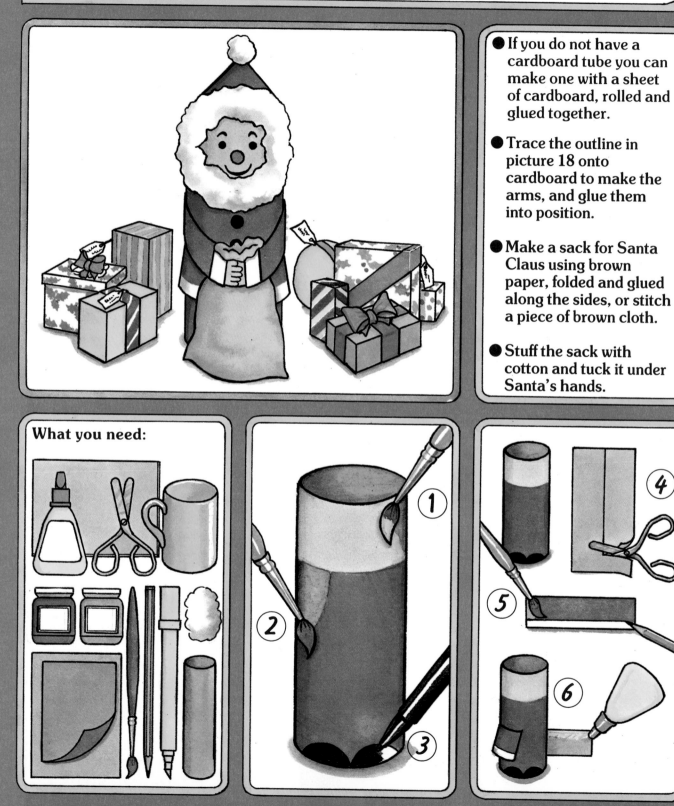

- If you do not have a cardboard tube you can make one with a sheet of cardboard, rolled and glued together.

- Trace the outline in picture 18 onto cardboard to make the arms, and glue them into position.

- Make a sack for Santa Claus using brown paper, folded and glued along the sides, or stitch a piece of brown cloth.

- Stuff the sack with cotton and tuck it under Santa's hands.

What you need:

Reindeer and Sleigh

- Trace the outline of the runner twice and of the reindeer's body once.

- The tray from a large matchbox is best for the sleigh, but any box of similar size will work.

- The heavy lines of the reindeer show where to cut, the dotted line where to fold.

What you need:

Paper Garlands

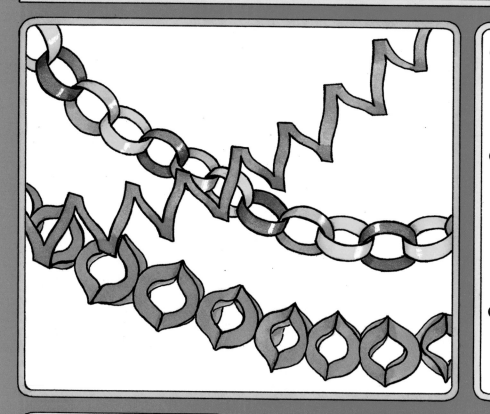

- Use any sort of colored paper to make these garlands – even patterned wrapping paper will do.

- For the third garland, make lots of circles from the tracing outline. Or you can draw around a teacup for the outer ring and an eggcup for the inner ring to make a bigger garland.

- If you have no colored paper, paint lots of plain paper in bright colors before you start.

What you need:

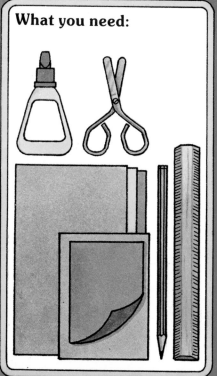

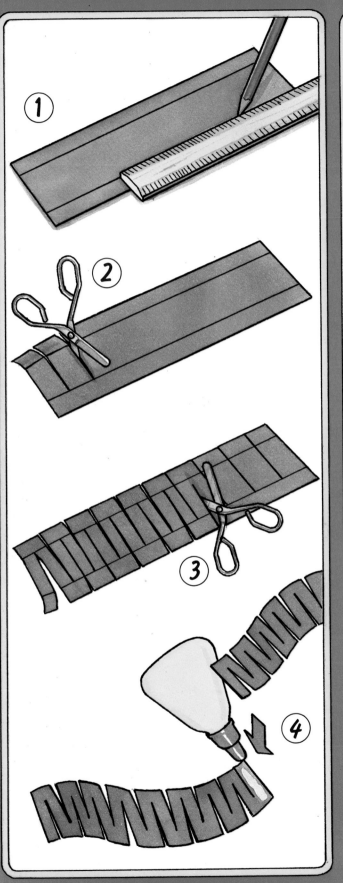

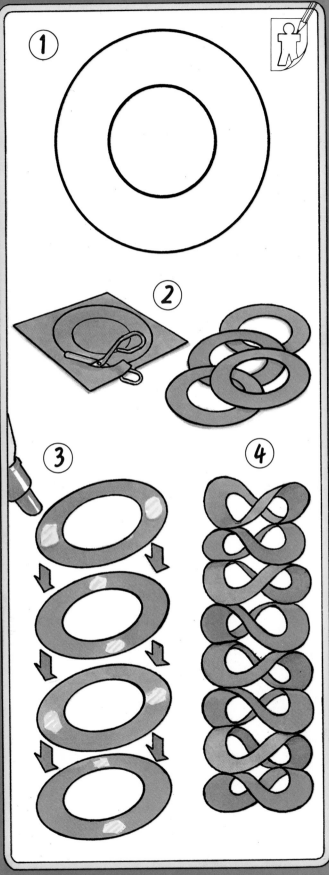

Tree Decorations

- Trace the star outline onto cardboard. If you do not have a pipe cleaner, you can hang the decoration with string or thread.

- Paint any design onto cardboard to make the lantern.

- When making the Christmas ball, be sure to attach the pipe cleaner (or thread secured with a knot) before gluing together the two halves.

What you need:

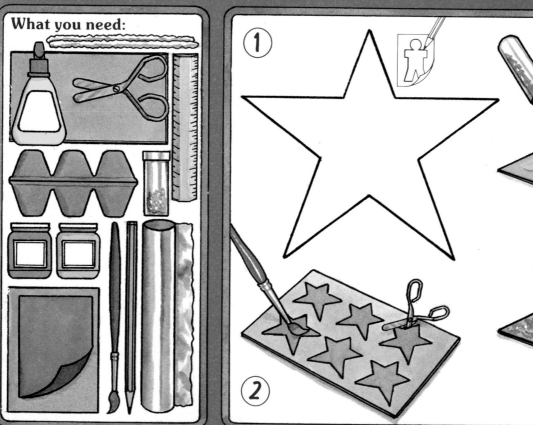

112

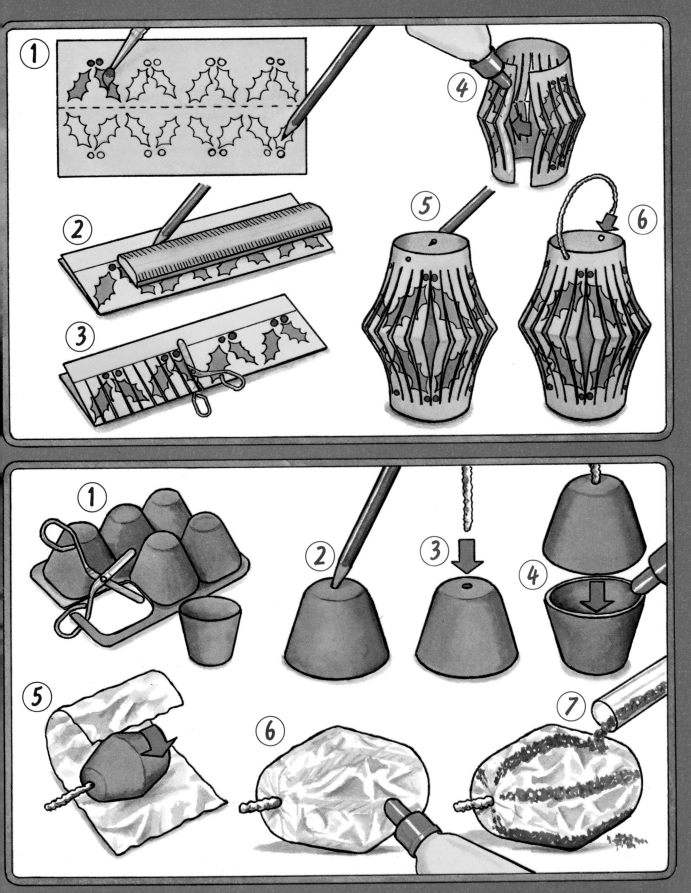

Snowman

- Trace the outline in picture 9 to make the brim for the hat, or draw around an eggcup.

- Any sort of bottle top will work for the top of the hat. Or mold modeling clay into shape and paint the brim in the same color.

- Use buttons, beads, or painted pieces of paper to decorate the snowman.

- You can use a twig for the walking stick if you do not have a pipe cleaner.

What you need:

① ②

③

Christmas Cards

- Paint decorations on the outside of the Christmas tree card and write your message inside.

- Trace the outline of the angel card. The solid lines show where you cut, the dotted lines show where you fold. Press the scissors through the card and cut only around the solid lines of the angel.

- Trace the hexagon shape three times onto a card, arranged as shown.

What you need:

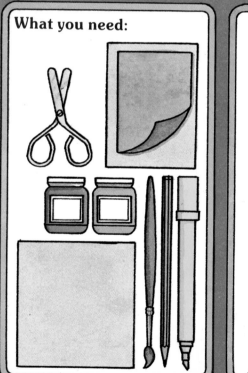

① ② ③ ④

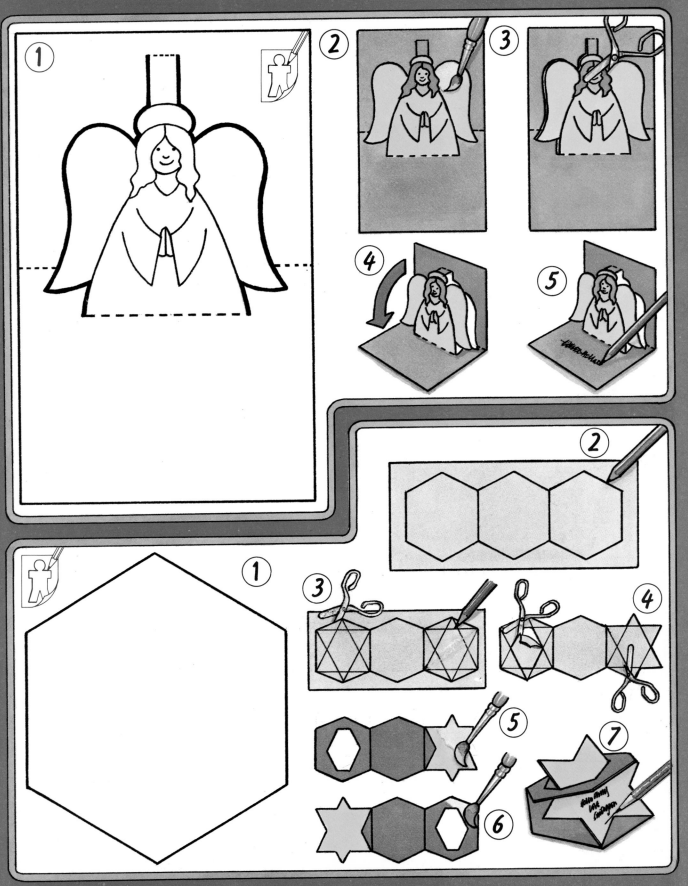

Christmas Tree

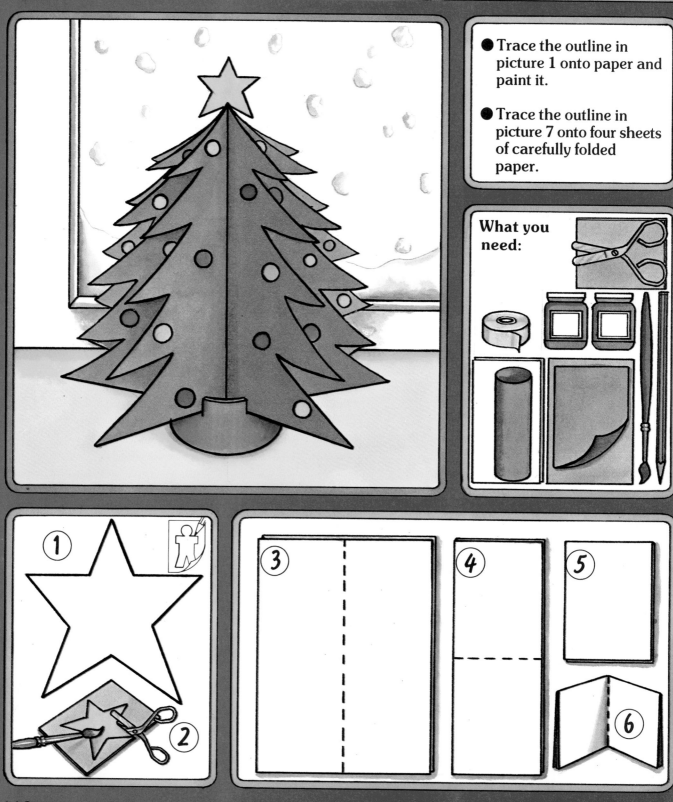

● Trace the outline in picture 1 onto paper and paint it.

● Trace the outline in picture 7 onto four sheets of carefully folded paper.

What you need:

① ② ③ ④ ⑤ ⑥

118

Lamb

- Used matchsticks are ideal for the legs but toothpicks can be used instead.

- Use any bottle top of suitable size – one from a toothpaste tube is perfect.

- Make the tail from a pipe cleaner or roll a piece of cotton between your fingers to make a tail shape and glue it into position.

What you need:

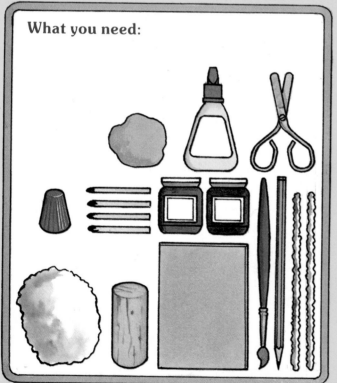

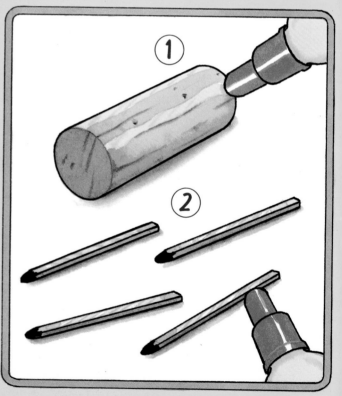

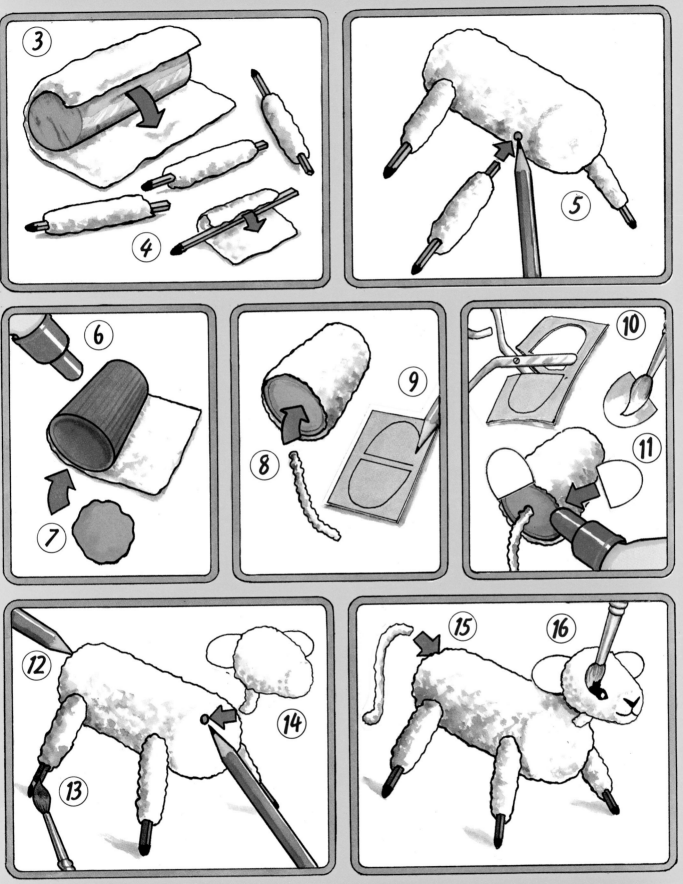

Donkey

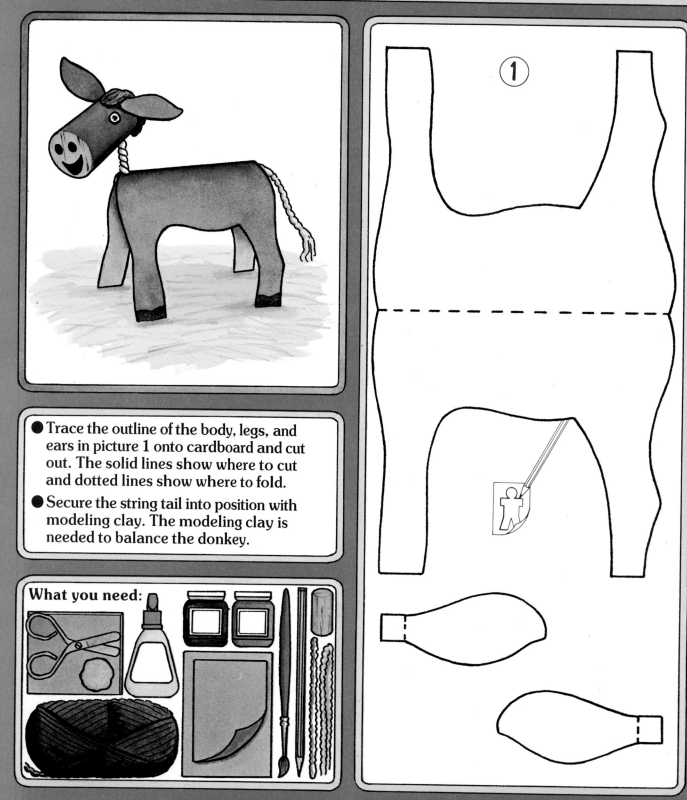

- Trace the outline of the body, legs, and ears in picture 1 onto cardboard and cut out. The solid lines show where to cut and dotted lines show where to fold.
- Secure the string tail into position with modeling clay. The modeling clay is needed to balance the donkey.

What you need:

122

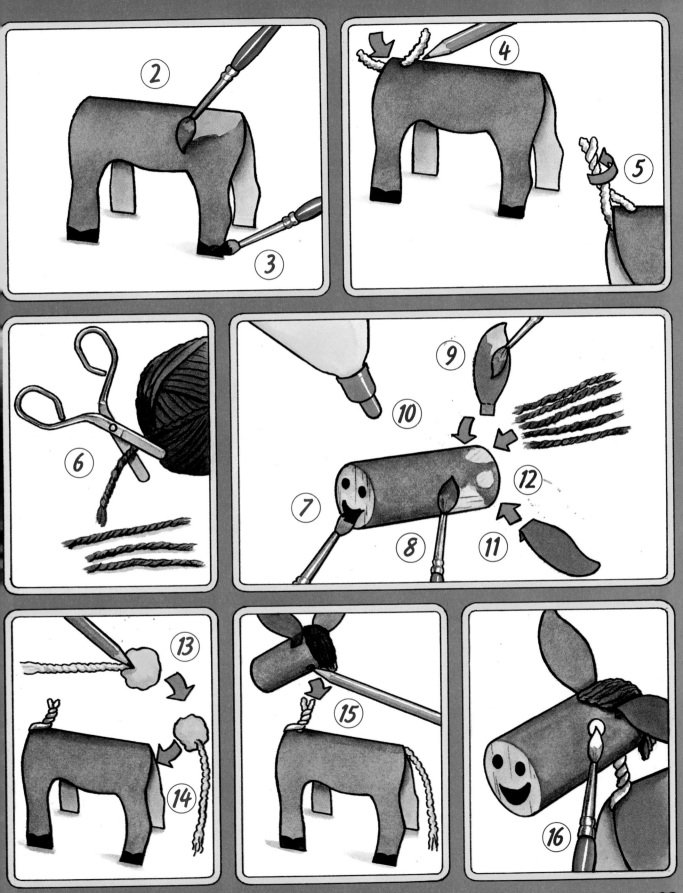

Mary and Joseph

- Use examples from pages 106 and 114 to make cone bodies.

- Paint the bodies in different colors and stick on shapes from tin-foil or paper lace doilies.

- Paint yellow circles of card as haloes for Mary and Joseph.

- Use scraps of cloth for the cloaks and knitting yarn or cotton for hair and beards.

What you need:

①

②

Shepherd and Three Kings

The Stable